A Modeler's Guide to

NAVAL ARCHITECTURE

by A. Richard Mansir

A Moonraker Publication

Dana Point, California

Published in the United States of America by
Moonraker Publications, 24452 B Alta Vista,
Dana Point, California, USA.

ISBN 0-940620-04-9

Printed and bound in the United States of America.

TABLE OF CONTENTS

THE MAKERS OF THIS BOOK

Written and Illustrated by A. Richard Mansir

Executive Administrator   D. J. Roberts

Ship models by:

     Henry W. Bridenbecker
     Donald C. Dressel
     Howard Judson
     Robert L. Pranka
     Arthur "Art" Robinson
     Richard Roos
     Allan Weiss

Star of India photography courtesy of the Maritime Museum Association of San Diego

Photography
     Greg Smith   San Diego, Ca

Color Separations
     Color Bar Corporation   Anaheim, Ca

Printing
     The Ink Spot   Ontario, Ca

INTRODUCTION

Fine ship modeling depends to a large extent on the modeler's understanding of his subject which at bottom is the engineering science known as naval architecture.

As a modeler comes to a given set of ship plans he is often dismayed as much by what is **not** given as what is, requiring that he fall back on his own imagination and knowledge to fill in or interpret details. In other words, he is obliged to project himself, as much as possible, into the role of a naval architect whose job it is (and was) to define each part of a ship for optimum performance. So what are the naval architect's thought processes? How did he approach his task at different periods in the past?

This book is intended to provide a background understanding of the science as we know it today. We trace its development from the seventeenth century during which period we find the first attempts to apply the principles of scientific inquiry to ship design. We describe the design methodology of these early shipwrights whose ideas dominated the ship designer's thinking until well into the 1800's when at last traditional concepts gave way to true, modern experimental science.

The illustrations, including photos of models and representative lines drawings, provide comparisons between ships of earlier and later vintages. In them one can see the radical change that took place in ship design through the nineteenth century.

Beside hull design considerations, we discuss some of the structural characteristics of ships of the separate periods, comparing iron and wood as building material.

Special thanks are due to Dave Brierley and Commander Bill Benson, curators of the Maritime Museum Association of San Diego for their expert advice and assistance in obtaining hard-to-come-by information; to the Ship Modeler's Association of Fullerton, California, and the Ship Modeler's Guild of San Diego for the use of their models as photographic subjects; and to Dee Roberts who has so superbly managed the array of administrative detail associated with this effort.

PRINCIPLES OF NAVAL ARCHITECTURE

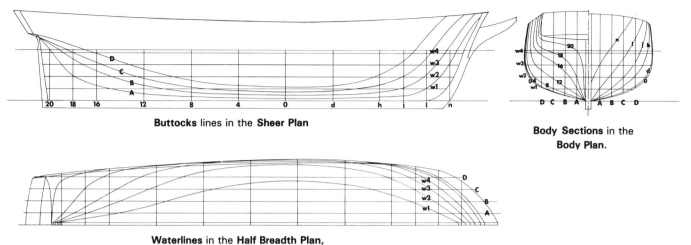

Buttocks lines in the **Sheer Plan**

Body Sections in the
Body Plan.

Waterlines in the **Half Breadth Plan,**

A ship's hull is described by the lines drawings.

Modern naval architecture relies on a body of scientific thought and technology which modern model builders bring into play primarily in the development and reading of plans. Historians and archaeologists record and expand upon the remains of ancient ships in the terms of contemporary ship designers as a way of coming to understand what the old ships looked like, how they must have performed, and how they were built.

Prior to 1550 very little of the shipwright's craft was set to paper. Plans, at least in the modern sense, were non-existent. Shipbuilders were hard-handed craftsmen whose closely guarded skills passed down through generations by word-of-mouth and practical experience. Few of these men were literate.

Ship design followed traditional principles. Upon acceptance of a commission to build a ship, a shipwright would set to work on his lofting floor, laying out full scale the frames and other components with straight edge and compasses according to arcane "rules" he learned from his father, and his father before him.

As one might expect, some of these old ships were catastrophic failures, but more surprising is the fact that so many succeeded. Our unsophisticated ancestors were far from lacking insight into the "way of a ship in the sea." We may appreciate their achievements better in the light of our present knowledge.

THE DRAFTING OF HULL LINES

BACKGROUND

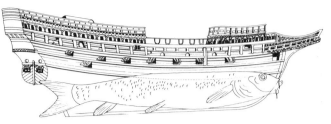

Mathew Baker, Henry the Eighth's "Master Shipwright" believed a ship should "go in like a Cod and out like a Mackeral."

During the 1500's, the Italian city states of Florence, Genoa and Venice harbored the genius of Renaissance Europe and, among other artists, spawned the leading shipwrights of the day. When Henry VIII became King of England in 1509, he perceived a need for warships able to mount "stone gonnes of yron upon trotill wheles" and "great bumberdes of brasse upon trotill wheles." Initially, his perception led to the creation of the *Henry Grace a Dieu*, the first of a line of great ships which eventually established England as mistress of the seas. But for all that, though the *Henry Grace a Dieu* was a great ship for her day, she was designed and built by traditional technologies. She proved cumbersome and unwieldly as a gun platform.

Henry hired some Italians steeped in the intellectual and artistic ferment that had nourished Leonardo da Vinci, among others. They brought to England the newly evolved methods of technical illustration which the great master himself had pioneered together with Filippo Brunelleschi, Leon Battista Alberti, and other maestri of quattrocento Italy. The Italians set to work to solve Henry's problem, and in 1546 the first four truly functional gun ships were launched.

At the same time Henry established a new school of naval architecture in England, taught by the Italians, and created the office of His Majesty's "Master Shipwright." Mathew Baker became the first to wear the title in 1572. His sketches and drafts are the earliest known technical drawings of the lines of a vessel, though we must presume that he learned to make them from his Italian tutors.

Baker's drafting skills, however, were exceptional among shipwrights even long after his death. While the practice gained some in popularity and technique, shipwrights continued to rely on their old methods. Baker, as the King's top man, after all represented the best of the elite in matters of shipbuilding, as did his successors.

Baker died in 1613 having survived Henry, witnessed the defeat of the Spanish Armada in 1588 and saw the passing of the great age of Elizabeth the First. James I reigned in England when Baker's duties were assumed by Phineas Pett and William Burrell.

Pett and Burrell, no doubt, were competent draftsmen in the manner of Baker, but Pett impressed King James with his design for the *Prince Royal*, not with drawings, but with a model. After Pett, models served shipwrights as much as drawings right up to our own day, and, often as not, were the only plans the builders in the yard had to go by. Burrell died in 1630. Pett became "Principal Officer and Commissioner" for the Navy. Shortly thereafter the rest of his shipbuilding family were happily employed under fat government contracts. Peter senior, a nephew, became master at Deptford; Peter junior, his son, became Navy commissioner at Chatham; while Christopher, his second son, set up shop at Woolwich and Deptford, and last, his grandson, Phineas, finally took over at Chatham. The dynasty ended in 1678 upon the death of Phineas, the younger.

The prevailing influence of the Petts through the century did little to promote ship design on paper. Their contribution to ship architecture (which was considerable as we shall see) lay elsewhere.

Their reign, however, gave rise to a new star, Anthony Deane. Deane's *Doctrine of Naval Architecture* appeared about 1675 and for the first time we see the subject of English shipbuilding treated with academic rigor and clarity.

Deane's work not only established naval architectural drafting as a norm, but applied mathematics and the new methods of scientific inquiry to the business of shipbuilding.

MODERN DRAFTING OF HULL LINES

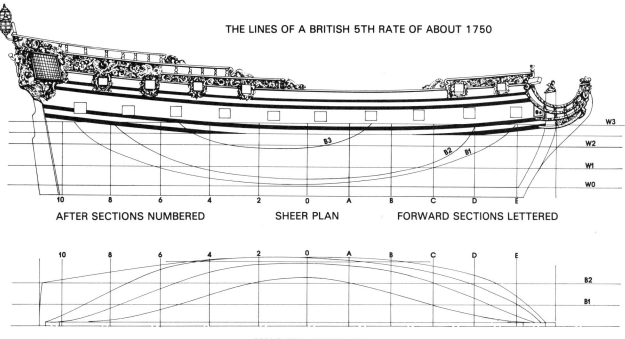

THE LINES OF A BRITISH 5TH RATE OF ABOUT 1750

AFTER SECTIONS NUMBERED   SHEER PLAN   FORWARD SECTIONS LETTERED

HALF BREADTH PLAN

From Deane's time to the present, marine architects have employed a more or less standard technique for the depiction of a three-dimensional hull form on paper. The delineations include a side view called the "sheer plan"; one-half of the top view called the "half breadth plan"; and an end view which shows one-half of each end in the same drawing called the "body plan."

The hull is visualized within a three-dimensional coordinate grid system referenced to a base line under the keel, a vertical line at the midship section, and the longitudinal centerline.

The lines of the sheer plan are called "buttocks." They represent the hull as if sliced vertically and longitudinally at increments measured out from the longitudinal centerline.

The half breadth plan delineates the "waterlines." They show the hull sliced horizontally at increments measured up from the keel base line.

The end view shows the "body sections," transverse vertical slices spaced fore and aft from the midship section. The midship section defines the widest section in the hull and does not

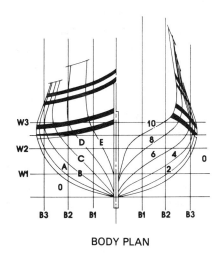

BODY PLAN

necessarily lie at the geometric center of the design.

Independent of the three sets of lines above, one may find one or more "diagonals" which represent the hull sliced longitudinally on a plane diagonal to the rest.

Finally, there may be a "displacement" curve which represents the distribution of the ship's underwater volume.

DISPLACEMENT

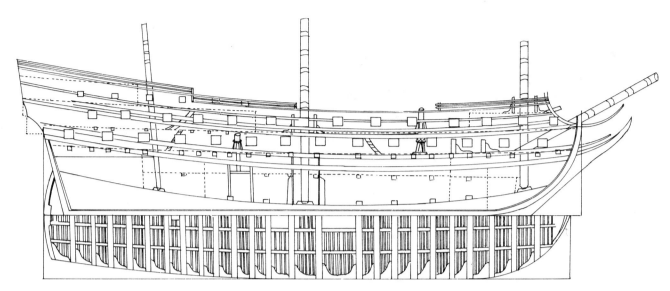

Sir Anthony Deane laid the foundation for modern architectural drafting. This longitudinal section drawing of a seventeenth century 3rd rate appeared in his *Doctrine of Naval Architecture* published in 1670.

Ships through most of history have been designated, taxed, and hired out by some measurement of their carrying capacities. Where other dimensions such as length, beam or depth of hold are ignored, a ship's "burthen" or tonnage is given as the key indicator of her size.

Originally a "tun" referred to a cask of wine of a dimension roughly equivalent in weight to a modern ton. A ship's "tunnage" therefore indicated the number of such tuns of wine she could carry. Later the "tun" became "ton" which referred not to a specific cargo, but to the actual total weight of the ship when loaded to her maximum. The total actual weight of a ship is designated by her displacement tonnage, since the weight of an object is exactly equal to the weight of the water it can "displace" or move aside when emersed.

Since a ton of water occupies about 35 cubic feet of space, knowledge of a ship's tonnage also gives us a rough idea of her other dimensions. For example, as we know that a 50-ton ship must displace 1750 cubic feet of space below the waterline, we must assign her a length, breadth and depth sufficient to accommodate such a volume. Hence, we can visualize a nicely proportioned vessel of perhaps 45 feet in length, 11 feet in beam with a draft of 5½ or 6 feet depending on the shape of her bottom.

Today the computation of a ship's displacement on the drawing board is a matter of course. But before the seventeenth century the mathematics for the computation were unknown. A ship's displacement was a matter to be settled after she was afloat.

As long as ships were built by the old conventions, the shipwrights could somewhat predict how a hull would float. He depended on the "school of hard knocks."

Trouble ensued, however, with Henry VIII's huge experimental vessels. Floating high out of the water and round as a log below water, many of the early gun ships sailed as cranky as corks. The problem was partially rectified by "girdling and firring," the practice of adding extra layers of planking around the waterline, but this was makeshift at best. Naval architecture required a new approach.

Events taking place in England around 1600, however, were about to revolutionize not only naval architecture, but every nail of human activity. Multitudes of problems in ship design, navigation and industry generally were to yield to the new philosophies of inductive and mathematical science.

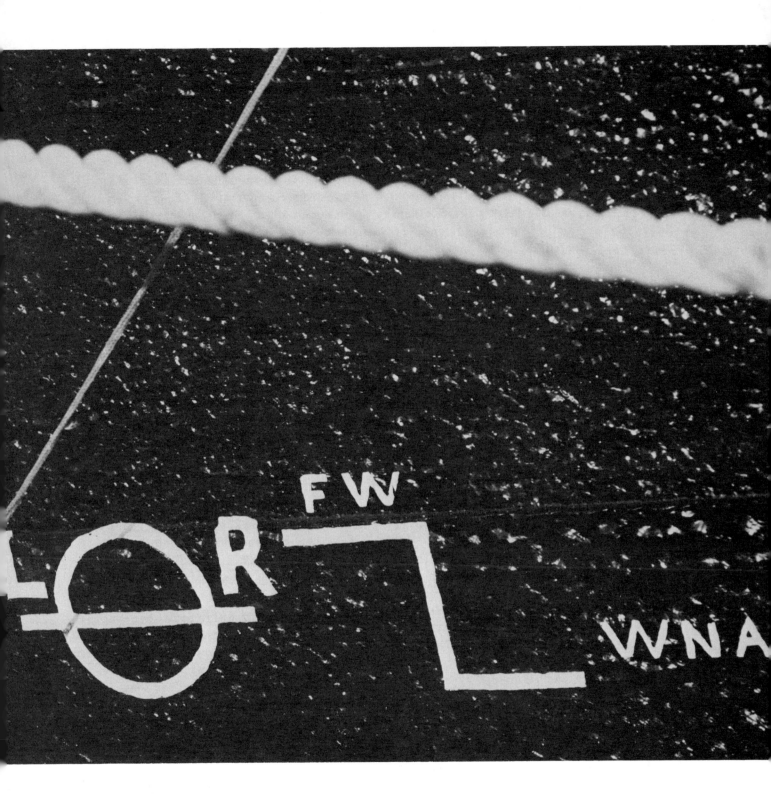

Plimsoll marks on the side of a vessel indicate her safe loading levels. They were mandatory markings for all merchant ships insured by Lloyds of London after 1876. The 'L R' means Lloyd's Register. The line marked FW indicated the fresh water load limit; WNA means the load limit for "winter North Atlantic." Other marks include 'W' (winter seawater), 'S' (summer seawater), 'T' (tropical seawater), and 'TF' (tropical fresh water). The different safe loading levels are specified because ships are more or less bouyant depending on the kind of water that supports them. A ship floats highest in cold salt water (WNA), and the lowest in warm fresh water (TF).

In 1598, across the Thames from the naval base at Deptford (East Greenwich), Gresham College was founded under the terms of the will of Sir Thomas Gresham, Queen Elizabeth's famous financial advisor. The new college soon became the meeting ground and clearing house for a new breed of scientific scholar committed to mathematics and experiment. A half century later in 1662, the "Royal Society of London" was incorporated on the foundation laid by the Gresham College scholars and professors. Among the lights who participated here early in the 1600's were William Gilbert, the famous experimenter with magnets; Henry Briggs, who computed the Briggsian tables of logarithms; William Oughtred, the inventor of the slide rule; and Edmund Gunter, who computed the logarithms of the trigonometric functions. Also included in this group were John Wells, keeper of His Majesty's Naval Stores at Deptford; and the master shipwrights, Phineas Pett, Edward Stevens, Hugh Lydiard, and Henry Goddard.

Gresham College may rightly be called the nursery of modern science. Within it the ideas of

Francis Bacon and Rene Descarte bloomed into those of Leibniz and Isaac Newton. And right in the midst of this towering ferment, spurring it on, were the navigators and shipbuilders seeking, among other things, an answer to the displacement problem.

Given that old Phineas Pett himself was engaged in Gresham College investigations, it is perhaps surprising that the first to solve the displacement question was none of the Petts, but again Anthony Deane. Deane's successful prediction of the waterline of a ship was what earned him his promotion to the top of his profession.

The exact computation of a ship's displacement tonnage is a subtle piece of mathematics, which at bottom is a problem in calculus. We may be duly impressed with Deane's accomplishment in 1666 when we realize that Leibniz did not publish his invention of the calculus until 1684 nor Newton his until 1687. We cannot, of course, credit Deane with having outdone either of these two mathematical geniuses, but we may suppose that he employed methods that set the stage for them.

REGISTER TONNAGE

Calculus, though, however valuable it became to the likes of physical scientists and engineers, remained an enigma to practical men of business as well as less recondite seamen. A more accessible computation of a ship's size was required for their purposes. Before Deane, a ship's tonnage was roughly computed by a formula. A ship's length in feet times her maximum beam in feet times her depth of hold (bottom of main deck to top of keel) all divided by 100 equaled her tonnage for taxing purposes.

$$\frac{L \times B \times D}{100} = \text{tonnage}$$

After Deane, in 1694, the formula was revised. Instead of dividing the product L x B x D by 100, one now divided by 94.

This rough and ready formula held standard until 1773 when the British Parliament enacted a new one, which thereafter became known as the "Builder's Old Measurement" (BOM). The BOM took the length of keel from the foreside of the

stem to the afterside of the sternpost as the starting number and declared a ship's tonnage to be:

$$\frac{L - 3/5 B \times B \times 1/2 B}{94}$$

None of these figures bore resemblance to actual displacement tonnage but rather sought to describe a ship's carrying capacity. The formulas provided the businessmen what they recognized as a ship's "register tonnage."

Later the formula for register tonnage was revised again eventually coming down to a matter of dividing all the load carrying space in a ship (expressed in cubic feet) by 100. The last was called deadweight tonnage.

Each of the nations of the world employ their own formulas for register tonnage. Thus a ship of a given tonnage from the U.S. would find itself assigned a different number while going through the Panama Canal and still another upon arrival at Le Havre. The complexities of the issue derive from the prevailing economic conditions of international trade.

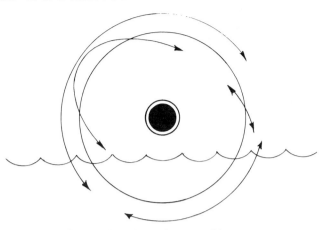

Center of gravity and center of buoyancy
coincide in a beach ball. Ball spins
and twirls.

The laws of buoyancy and gravity play an extremely important role in the design of a ship. The laws of gravity, of course, account for the ship's weight and her displacement tonnage as discussed above. A ship's buoyancy, on the other hand, has to do with the counter force that keeps the vessel afloat.

In the simplest terms, a ship is buoyant so long as the total weight of her hull is less than the weight of the water she displaces. As long as this condition holds the ship is said to have "positive buoyancy." When the total weight of the ship exceeds the weight of water displaced, we have "negative buoyancy," and the ship sinks.

Submarines are vessels equipped to vary their buoyancy between positive and negative. When the water is allowed into the ballast tanks its weight is added to the rest of the ship until neutral or negative buoyancy is achieved and the sub dives. In surfacing, the ballast tanks are pumped out and positive buoyancy returns.

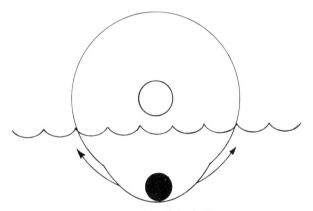

A weight on one side of the ball separates
centers. Ball is stabilized with 'up' and
'down' sides.

It is not enough, however, to simply make a ship "float." "How" it floats is as important to her performance as the fact itself. We may come to appreciate the marine architect's concern with the question through some elementary illustrations.

If we throw a beach ball into a swimming pool it certainly floats, but it also bobs and spins about without regard for which side is up. A beach ball, even though it floats, makes a poor ship.

We could improve the situation a little if we fastened a weight to one side of the ball. Doing this would move the center of gravity more to one side than the other, and the heavier side would sink giving us an 'up' side. The heavier we make the weight, the less is the likelihood that the ball will roll over. If we fasten the weight to the ball by a string, the system becomes even more stable.

Now the center of buoyancy in the beach ball is the very center of it, and as long as we have attached no weights to it, that point is also its center of gravity. So it is clear that a vessel whose center of gravity coincides with its center of buoyancy is a highly unstable affair.

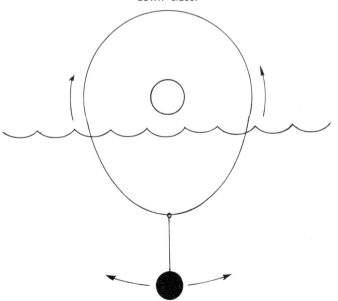

Separating centers even more increases
stability even more.

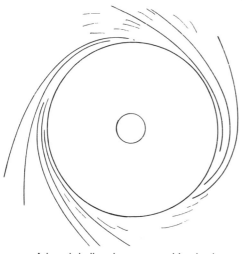

A beach ball makes a poor ship also because it spins like a top and cannot be steered.

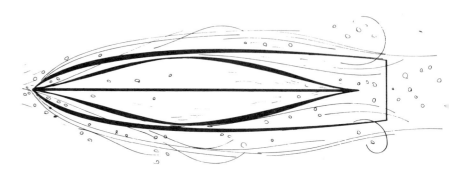

A ship needs to be longer one way than the other to reduce drag in the fore and aft direction while increasing the resistance of her sides.

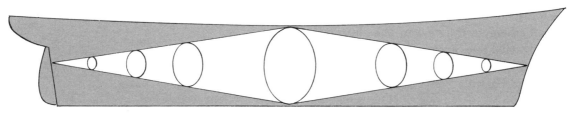

A ship is more buoyant amidships than at either of her ends because of the difference in the volume of air in these various locales. Structural strength is required to keep the two ends from sagging or "hogging."

As we add weight, first to one side of the ball and then to the end of an attached string, we progressively add to the distance between the two centers and thereby make it more and more difficult to force the up side, down.

Thus the hull of a ship becomes more and more stable as its center of gravity is removed from the center of buoyancy.

A beach ball, even if ballasted, makes a poor ship for another reason. It has no bow and no stern and so has an inclination to spin around like a top. A ship, on the other hand, is required to go somewhere and must be designed to accommodate this requirement. For this reason, ships are longer than they are wide, have pointed, wedge-shaped bows, and long keels which cut the water one way and offer solid resistance to it the other. We shall deal with these shapes more later, but for the moment we must consider how they affect the questions of buoyancy and weight.

If we were to float a vessel shaped like an ice cream cone, we would find that it would tend to float with the point end down. This would happen because the greater displacement volume, and hence the center of buoyancy, would lie in the larger end.

The hull of a ship corresponds, more or less, to the shape of two ice cream cones set end to end with the big ends facing each other. The center of buoyancy is midships, but the two point ends, like the ice cream cones, are inclined to sink and would if the ship were not structurally solid enough to prevent it.

Those intimate with ships recognize the structural failure associated with this principle as "hogging." As an old ship approaches the end of her days, her structure weakens and her bow and stern droop lower in the water and she is evermore condemned as "hog backed" or "floating on a broken back."

THE CENTER OF GRAVITY

As we have said, the farther apart we can separate the center of gravity from the center of buoyancy in the vertical plane, the more stable is the ship. But where do we place it in the fore and aft direction? The answer depends for the most part on the means of propulsion, which, in our inquiry, is limited to sails.

If we have a weight to move we have the choice of either pushing it from behind or pulling it from ahead. Either way can work depending on circumstances. But if we have a situation in which our objective is to push a long stick through the water on a straight course it will be seen that trying to push it from astern becomes something of a balancing act, while dragging it presents fewer problems. So it is with sailing ships. A ship whose concentration of sail area is aft of her center of gravity is nigh impossible to steer (though there are circumstances when sails would be so set). The effect is rather like trying to push a strand of spaghetti through a keyhole. So one is not surprised to find that the center of gravity on a sailing ship is invariably aft of the center of effort of her sails.

Other than this, the location of a ship's center of gravity is a matter of maintaining her trim. Some ships trim "down by the head"; others "down by the stern," often at the inclination of the skipper who loads and stows ballast or cargo.

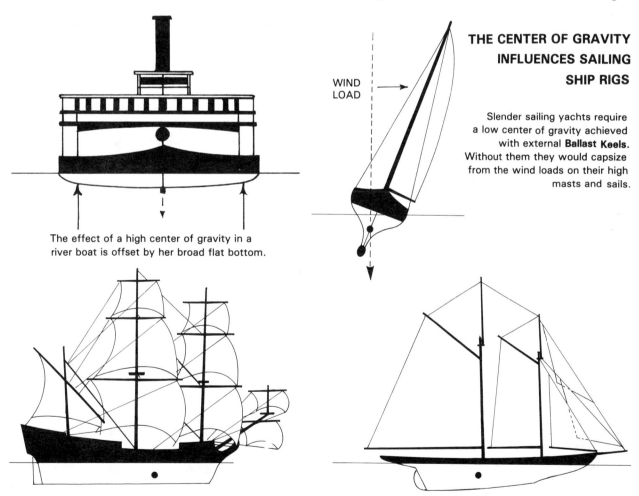

The effect of a high center of gravity in a river boat is offset by her broad flat bottom.

WIND LOAD

THE CENTER OF GRAVITY INFLUENCES SAILING SHIP RIGS

Slender sailing yachts require a low center of gravity achieved with external **Ballast Keels**. Without them they would capsize from the wind loads on their high masts and sails.

More forward center of gravity of seventeenth century ships required more forward placement of sails.

As the center of gravity moved aft so did the center of effort of the sails.

LATERAL RESISTANCE

The area of lateral resistance is the portion of the hull's surface which is vertical and broadside below water. Lateral resistance is provided by the keel plus the portion of the ship sides below the waterline. A larger area of lateral resistance reduces the tendency of a ship to be blown sideways.

A sailing ship requires a larger area of lateral resistance to offset the effect of winds blowing against her high sails.

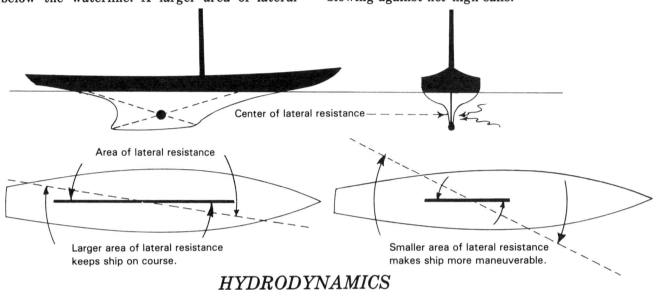

Center of lateral resistance

Area of lateral resistance

Larger area of lateral resistance keeps ship on course.

Smaller area of lateral resistance makes ship more maneuverable.

HYDRODYNAMICS

Hydrodynamics is the branch of physics that deals with the flow of fluids around solid bodies. The first published investigations in the science, as we know it, are attributable to Daniel Bernoulli whose *Hydrodynamica* appeared in 1738. In this work, Bernoulli advanced the kinetic theory of gases and fluids, in which he set forth a now famous formula known as Bernoulli's equation. The equation in effect accounts for the rate of flow of fluids (liquids or gases) over the surfaces of objects immersed in them. The equation has played a role not only in ship design, but in the design of airplanes, pipelines, oil refineries, chemical plants, and every other segment of technology where gases and liquids interface with solids.

Bernoulli's work, however, dealt with a more general problem than the specific task of ship design. Practical naval architecture involved many more considerations than those he addressed.

The question for ship designers is what is the most effective shape for a hull that can be devised for the job at hand? Among the first to address the question with scientific rigor was Sir Isaac Newton. Sir Isaac declared that the best shape for a ship was that of a teardrop or perhaps a dolphin's body. He was right except that he overlooked the fact that a surface ship was only partly underwater and, therefore, did not behave as his calculations showed. Sir Isaac defined the shape of a modern submarine. His theory was ahead of its time. It was William Froude, between 1868 and 1870, who finally laid down the theoretical principles behind modern hull design.

The early shipwrights devised hull shapes intuitively and by trial and error. They recognized that a round bottomed log rolled over and over, while an outrigger attached to the log stabilized the system. They knew that a blunt bow was harder to push through the water than a pointed, wedge-shaped one. And, finally, they could observe the shape of fish which seemed to have the problem of hydrodynamic efficiency rather well worked out. Thus the theory of hull design evolved, until we hear Mathew Baker in 1575 declaring that a ship should "go in like a cod, and out like a mackerel."

Baker's injunction, generally, held sway in the thinking of ship designers until well into the eighteenth century. It was this idea that continued the tradition of the slow and cumbersome bluff-bowed vessels that preceded the famous clipper ships.

The American shipwrights under compunction to create fast vessels capable of hit-and-run tactics, blockade running, and the like, developed the idea of sharp-bowed vessels. Such vessels found their first expression in the famed Baltimore clippers.

The sharp 'v' bottomed Baltimore clippers astonished the world with their sailing qualities in the years before and after the American War of 1812. But the quest for speed continued through the nineteenth century finally culminating in the still unbeaten sailing ship records set by the American clippers built in the early 1850's.

The hull designs of the clippers evolved through the experience and instinct of practical shipwrights and mariners more than theoretical science, however. As we have observed, William Froude did not enter the scene until 1868 when the day of the sailing ship was past its meridian.

Froude's contribution to naval architecture grew from his experiments with models in a towing tank. Through these experiments he was able to show a correlation between the behavior of models and full-sized ships, and identify the principle causes of resistance to a ship's progress through the water. From this he developed the now universal tenet of marine architecture known as 'wave line theory.'

Wave line theory is a rather complex bit of mathematics which correlates the wave patterns a hull creates at various speeds with the amount of friction present. Thus, if a model is towed in the tank at a specified speed, one can deduce the amount of drag or friction the hull is producing by observing the kind of waves it makes in the surrounding water.

With the theory, the marine architect can today predict optimal hull designs, power requirements, propeller size and dozens of other variables.

WAVE LINE THEORY

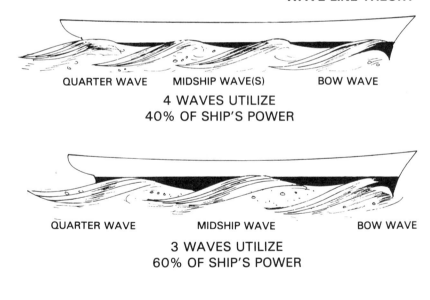

QUARTER WAVE   MIDSHIP WAVE(S)   BOW WAVE

4 WAVES UTILIZE
40% OF SHIP'S POWER

QUARTER WAVE   MIDSHIP WAVE   BOW WAVE

3 WAVES UTILIZE
60% OF SHIP'S POWER

QUARTER WAVE   BOW WAVE

2 WAVES EQUALS
MAXIMUM SPEED FOR
A DISPLACEMENT HULL

A ship's power plant must overcome two energy consuming forms of resistance -skin friction and wave-making resistance. At low speeds skin friction accounts for 95% of the drag in a hull. As speed increases the ship begins to make waves along each side becoming fewer in number the faster the ship goes. If a ship makes a four wave wash between bow and stern and her bottom is reasonably clean, she will be spending about 40% of her power output in making waves. A three wave wash accounts for 60%. A two wave wash implies about the maximum speed a given hull can achieve, because any faster and the boat would stand on end, stern down.

Fast, modern racing sailboats approach two wave washes in good sea and wind conditions. What a thrill a skipper gets when his stern runs awash in the lee quarter wave.

The amount of additional power needed to increase the speed of a vessel from three to two waves is much more than from four to three.

Few modern power-driven vessels can afford the horsepower for two wave washes, though the sailing clipper ships seem to have taken them in stride. The mathematics of wave line theory declare that a 225 foot ship would be sailing 21 knots in a two wave wash. Clippers of that length often exceeded 21 knots.

THE SIX COMPONENTS OF SHIP MOTION

At sea a ship is tossed and turned by waves, wind, and currents. The naval architect views these effects in terms of six kinds of movement and takes them into account when seeking the most efficient hull shape for a given seagoing task. For example, the hull of an aircraft carrier is designed for maximum stability at the expense of speed and maneuverability, while that of a destroyer is just the opposite.

The prescriptions given below for minimizing roll, pitch and so on are anything but absolute. They simply suggest the kind of trade-offs that enter the thoughts of the architect during the preliminary stages of hull design.

The final design of a hull evolves through a series of tests using models in a towing tank in a manner directly parallel to Froude's early experiments.

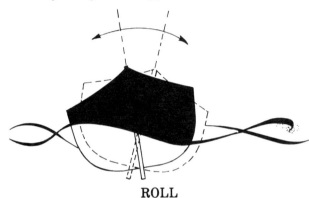

ROLL

Ship tips side to side. Roll may be minimized by increasing beam; increasing the straight area of lateral resistance; designing a more square body section; or lowering the center of gravity.

PITCH

Ship tips up and down like a seesaw in the fore and aft direction. Pitching may be minimized by concentrating the underwater bulk of the ship around the C.G. and increasing the buoyancy of the higher portions of bow and stern.

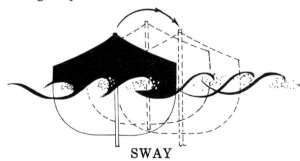

SWAY

Ship lifts up and to the side. Sway may be minimized by lowering the C.G., increasing the area of lateral resistance, or decreasing beam.

SURGE

Ship lifts up and forward. Surge may be minimized by distributing the underwater bulk of the ship along its length.

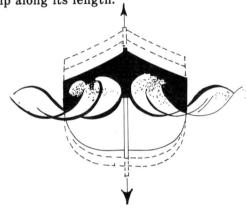

HEAVE

Ship lifts up and down parallel with the water. Heaving may be minimized by narrowing the beam, softening the chines, or spreading out the underwater bulk of the ship along its length. Minimizing heave could increase the tendency to pitch.

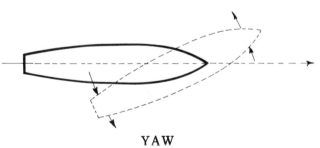

YAW

Ship pivots sideways to the line of her course. Yaw may be minimized by increasing the length to beam ratio and/or the area of lateral resistance.

DESCRIPTIVE TERMS

The naval architect uses a certain vocabulary to distinguish characteristic features and locales within a hull design.

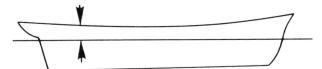

FREEBOARD — The height of a ship's sides above the waterline.

COUNTER — The underpart of the stern, above water, between the sternpost and the taffrail.

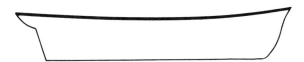

SHEER — the line of the deck or upper edge of the sheer strake as seen in profile. A strong or steep sheer line sweeps up in a curve fore and aft from a point midships. A flat sheer describes a more level deck line.

ENTRY — The shape of the bow and forward part of the hull at, and below, the waterline. A fine entry is a long, slender wedge gradually curving out to the full width of the ship. The old, bluff-bowed ships had "rough" or "hard" entries.

RUN — The shape of the afterbody below the waterline. A fine run tapers aft much as the entry does forward. A ship with a fine entry and run slides through the water with a minimum of turbulence.

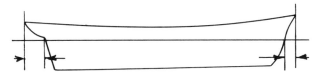

OVERHANG — The distance a ship's bow or stern hangs out over the water above the waterline.

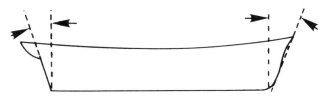

RAKE — The angle the stem or sternpost makes with the keel when viewed in profile. Also applied to masts, funnels and the like.

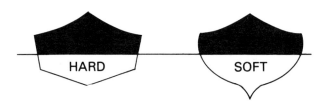

CHINE — The line of transition between the upper sides of the hull and its bottom. When sides and bottom come together at a sharp angle, the vessel is said to be "hard chined." If the transition is curved, the chines are "soft." Chines become softer as the radius of curve increases.

RISE OF FLOORS — The angle at which the floor timbers rise from the keel toward the sides. An acute 'v' bottomed hull is said to have strongly rising floors, while a more flat-bottomed vessel will have slowly rising ones.

17

ANTHONY DEANE'S DRAFTING PROCEDURE

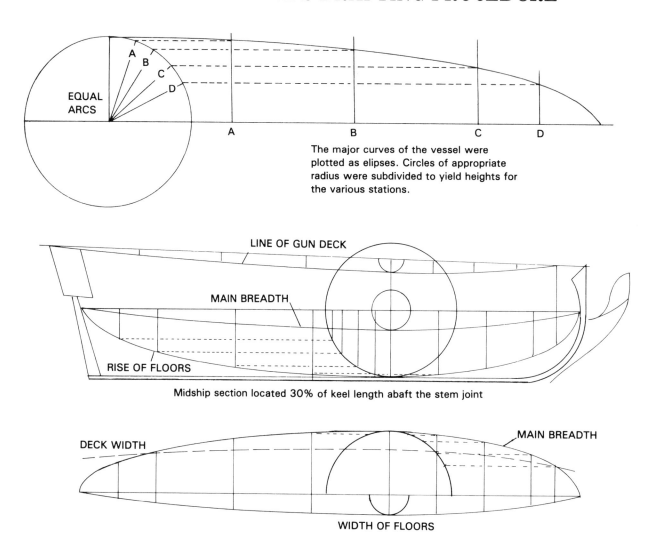

EQUAL ARCS

The major curves of the vessel were plotted as elipses. Circles of appropriate radius were subdivided to yield heights for the various stations.

LINE OF GUN DECK

MAIN BREADTH

RISE OF FLOORS

Midship section located 30% of keel length abaft the stem joint

DECK WIDTH

MAIN BREADTH

WIDTH OF FLOORS

Anthony Deane plotted the basic curves of the sheer and half breadth plans from circles drawn to appropriate sizes. Ninety degree arcs of the circles were subdivided into four or so smaller arcs yielding as many heights above the reference line. These heights then were projected to the body section lines to provide a point plot for the eliptical curves in question. The lines so plotted included the sheer line, rise of floors, and main deck line in the sheer plan; and the maximum breadth line, and width of floors line in the half breadth plan.

The body sections were located by first locating the midship section at a point about 30% of the keel length abaft of the joint between the keel and the stem. Then each of the fore and after sections were subdivided into four equal parts and the most forward and aft of these parts divided in two again.

The sizes of the circles from which the eliptical curves were plotted were in some cases defined by the ship's primary specifications (main breadth, for example), but otherwise were simply "eye balled" so as to yield curves that looked right to the designer.

With this much of the ship defined, Deane was ready to proceed to the drafting of the body sections which we will allow him to explain in his own words.

"Now all the lines are prepared for sweeping out the Midship Bend, I take from my scale one fourth part of my whole Breadth of my Shipp which is 9 foot and set one leg of my compasses in ye flower line at K and sweep it from H to L, this sweepe is called ye Flower Sweepe, haveing don with that I take 7/9 of the flower sweepe and sticke it under the Breadth line downeward from E to N and the Center M . . .

"Haveing prepared those two sweepes above mentioned I take of 20/36 of my breadth setting one leg of my compasses in O and strike the line. From L to N the sweepe is the sweepe with which maketh the upper and lower futtucke moulldes as you will peceave ere you have don . . .

"Haveing don all my sweepes under ye breadth I come unto my top timber; for which I take 17/18 of the half breadth which is seaventene foot setting one leg of my compasses in P and stricke ye sweepe from E to R, haveing don that I take the same sweepe and stricke a hollow for the head of the top timber, by the same radious the last was strucke by and sweepe out the hollow sweepe from S to R which sweepe compleates the bends of timber by which you are to make the moulds for two gradiate all the rest of the bends of timbers and for the whoulle Frame . . .

"One of the last place you were showne how ye half bends of timbers were swept out by wch you were to make your Moulds and being made with a good scarfe for every timber you are to proceed in yet sweeping out yet remaining parts of the ship afte as you find out one within another where ye shipp is compleated, but for feare raiseing them may be to dark for ye understanding I will show you one example more to make you p-fit and shall suppose I were to raise ye bend of timbers it is where I do thus. I look at my draft and take ye riseing from ye pole to ye line where it stands on ye draft wch I set of from ye line A, B and is ye line C, C, haveing done that, I take allso from my draft ye narrowing of my flower wch I set of ye line D. E and is yet line F. G this is ye

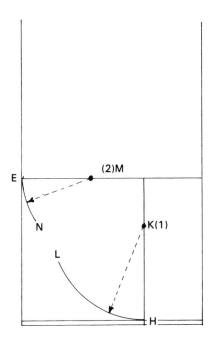

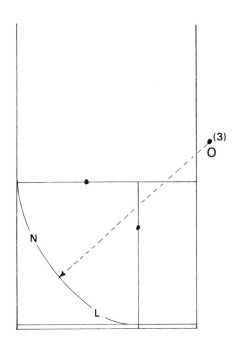

(1) Radius = 1/4 x beam
(2) Radius = 7/9 x (1)
(3) Radius = 20/36 x beam

narrowing of flower, haveing done that I take from my draft ye Height of Breadth at 15 wch I set of from ye line A, B, and is the line H, I, haveing done that I take from my draft ye narrowing of greatest breadth at 15 which I set of from I to H and yet like narrowing and riseing from ye top timber head which is ye line K, L, now haveing set of all ye narrowings and hights in every place I proced to swepe ye flower swepe 9 foot as ye former setting one leg of my compasses in P and sweeping under breadth from Q to R haveing don that I take the same 20 foot swepe of my Midship Bend and set one leg in S and swepe from R to O, haveing don that I keep my center all for ye top timbers as in ye Midships, setting one leg at T and swepe from Q to W and from that ye follow swepe as in ye other observing to fetch out ye hollow at ye stearne, all ye sweepes being thus struck you have ye 1/2 bends of timbers compleated at 15 in like mang and all the other . . .

"This latter is noe other than ye former for its nature of workeing onely as ye last was ye bend of timbers aftward on marked 15 this shall be a bend of timbers forward named N which is set of by ye narrowings and riseings as ye other onely as ye one is worked afte on the starboard side ye other is wrought on ye larboard side that one suite of moulds may serve your turne to builld by, as for example I look on ye drafte and take ye true riseing from N where it stands on ye keele to ye riseing line and set it of from ye line A, B which is ye line C, D, and this is ye riseing line, then I take from my drafte ye narrowing and set from ye line A, E which is the line F, G ye riseing and narrowing or ye breadth is the same as is often shewen, haveing thus done I proceed to sweepe by the same sweepes as above sweepeing out from H to I ye flower sweepe and from K to L under ye breadth from K to M above ye breadth and from M to N the top of the side, which I hope by this you see perfect the riseing of the whole ship's boddy in every part onely as you have these single ye other be one within as other as you will find in ye next place you come at as appear to your better sattisfaction . . ."

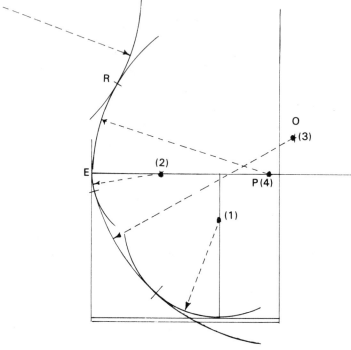

(1) Radius = 1/4 x beam
(2) Radius = 7/9 x (1)
(3) Radius = 20/36 x beam
(4) Radius = 17/18 x beam/2
(5) Radius = (4)

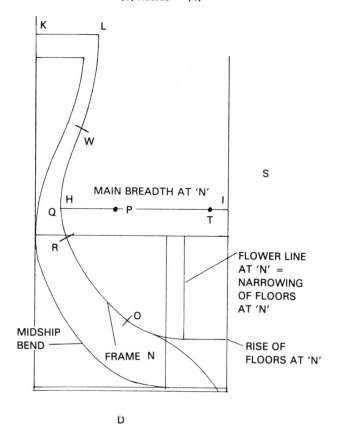

MAIN BREADTH AT 'N'

FLOWER LINE AT 'N' = NARROWING OF FLOORS AT 'N'

MIDSHIP BEND

FRAME N

RISE OF FLOORS AT 'N'

SUBSEQUENT FRAMES FOLLOW PROPORTIONALLY

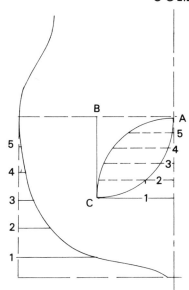

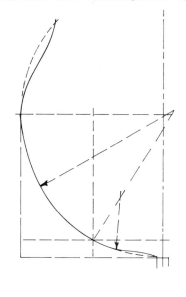

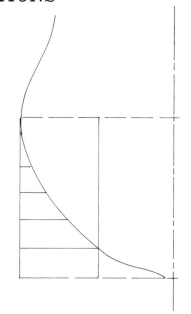

Full Built Ship in 1750
A-B was the key dimension in determining the fullness of a ship's body. An arc AC of smaller radius yields shorter lengths for the point plots of the body (distances 1, 2, 3, etc.) and produces a fuller ship. As AB increases, the distances 1, 2, 3,... become longer and a sharper ship results.

Round Bodied Ship 1750
This method of laying out the bends derives from Deane except that the flower sweep has a shorter radius. The narrowing of these ships above their maximum breadth was called *tumblehome*. Tumblehome was built into hulls to bring topsides more parallel with the run of the mast shrouds, to reduce the amount of deck exposed to boarding seas, and to make attack by boarding difficult.

Very Sharp Ship
A sharp vessel rode low in the water with a comparatively low center of gravity. Consequently she could carry a heavy press of sail with a hull that could ''bite'' the water and hold a course when other ships would drift to leeward. Among such sharp vessels as shown here were the famous American Baltimore clippers of the early 1800's.

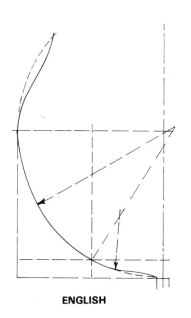

ENGLISH

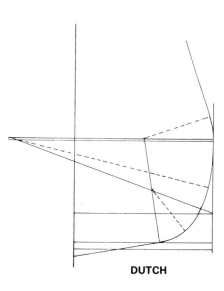

DUTCH

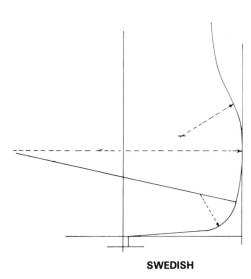

SWEDISH

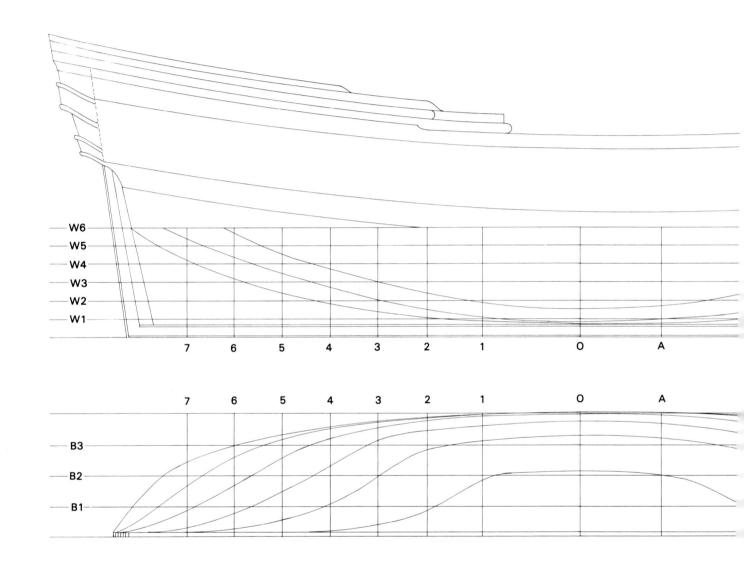

W6
W5
W4
W3
W2
W1

7   6   5   4   3   2   1   O   A

7   6   5   4   3   2   1   O   A

B3

B2

B1

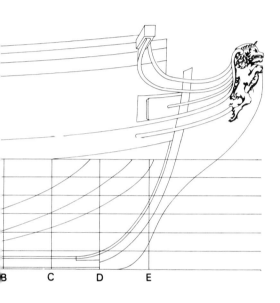

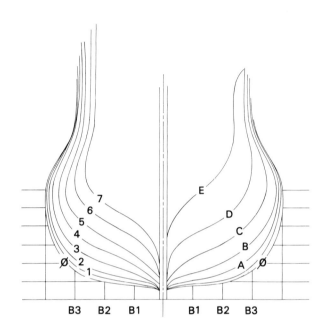

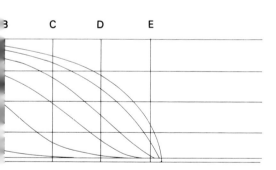

LINES OF HMS CENTURION
Launched Portsmouth, England 1732
A 4th Rate ship of 50 guns, Centurion sailed around the world in 1740-44 under the command
of Commodore George Anson. The voyage, among the earlier of English circumnavigations
around Cape Horn into the Pacific, cost 1300 lives out of Anson's squadron of six ships. Only
four were combat casualties. The rest died of disease. Centurion brought home 500,000
pounds in prize money taken from a Spanish treasure ship in the Philippines.

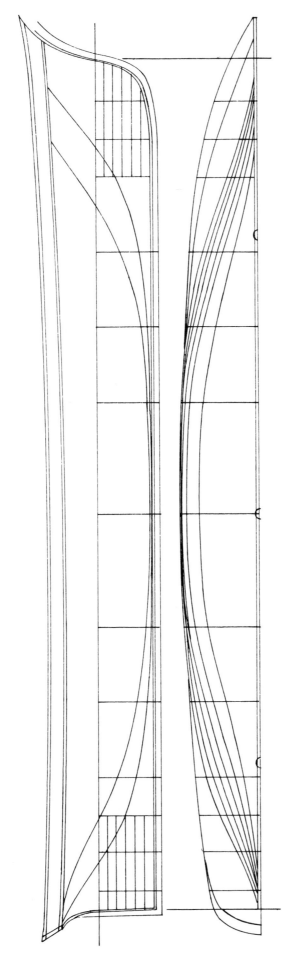

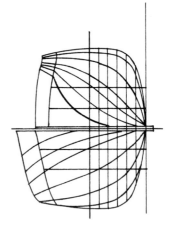

Lines of the American clipper **LIGHTNING** 1854 East Boston, 2084 tons 243 feet x 43 feet beam x 23 feet depth of hold. Designed and built by Donald Mackay.

The lines of the *Lightning* reveal the thinking of a later day when sailing ships reached their maximum levels of performance. Full, flat floors amidships provided a solid buoyancy and stability for a ship that otherwise was needle sharp at bow and stern. The *Lightning* once covered 436 miles in 24 hours averaging 18 knots per hour, a dramatic contrast to the ships of Deane's day that averaged three or four knots per hour and caused a sensation if they made six.

CLINKER BUILT
SHIPS

Scandinavian shipbuilders planked their vessels "clinker fashion." The planks overlapped one another like shingles. The *Kalmar Ship* of about 1250 A.D. shown here in a 3/8″ = 1′0″ model by H. Bridenbecker, was built shell first with 13 planks per side. Reinforcing frames, knees, and through beams were added after the planks were riveted together with iron nails. The windlass was used to raise and lower the mast and sails. The ship was 26½ feet long and 15 wide.

Clinker building is still used in construction of small boats to this day though carvel planking became the standard for large ships after 1600. Overlapped planks used more material and adapted themselves poorly to the more economical plank-on-frame methodologies because of the zigzag cross-section that was created with them.

BENT FRAME CONSTRUCTION

Small boats were built as lightweight craft with slender frames steamed and bent to fit the plank shell which was built first over supporting molds. Stringer, rubbing strakes, gunwales, and seat thwarts were added last. This 1/2'' = 1'0'' model of a ship's pinnace ca 1825 by Howard Judson was built the same way as the original.

Plank-on-frame built ships were planked carvel fashion or edge-to-edge so each plank lay firmly against the frames. Heavy inner frames supported a lighter skin of planking. The open spaces between the outer and inner (ceiling) planks were often filled with rock salt to inhibit rot. This model illustrates the plank-on-frame construction in perfect detail.

Model by H. Bridenbecker

CHINESE WAR JUNK ca 1850 - 1/8" = 1'0"
The Chinese shipwrights built oceangoing junks similar to the one shown here, before the time of Christ, while archeologists are beginning to think that Chinese navigators visited California as early as 300 A.D. Among other sophistications, junks featured watertight bulkheads dividing the ship into several independently buoyant sections - a safety measure not adopted by the West until Brunel built the *Great Britain* in 1843. This model represents a vessel 100 feet long by 25 feet in beam. She carried a crew of 200 men.

MALEK ADHEL - 1840, 1/4'' = 1'0''.

William Webb of New York figured as one of the greatest of American ship designers and builders of his era. The *Malek Adhel* was one of the many ships from his yard built for the China Trade. She was one of Webb's smaller efforts measuring 80 feet on deck, 20 feet in beam and 7 feet 9 inches depth of hold. Strongly rising floors and sharp entry and run recall the ''fast ship'' design ideas of the period between 1810 and 1845.

TANCOOK WHALER - ca 1900, 3/8" = 1'0"

Model by H. Bridenbecker

The Tancook islanders whose habitat lay off Nova Scotia, built an industry
supplying whale boats to the New England whaling fleet. They used their boat
building skills to make fine seaworthy fishing craft like this one for their own use.
Their lightweight construction, and pink sterns made them fast sailers and
especially good in following seas. This boat built about 1900 was 40 feet overall;
9'-8" in beam, with a 4'-2" draft with her centerboard down.

Model by R. Roos

PINKY SCHOONER - ca 1850, 1/4'' = 1'0''

Among the earlier U.S. fore and aft riggers were the pinky schooners like this one. They were the common ''poor man's'' fishing boat of the New England coasts between 1800 and 1850. Their unique features were the strong sheer, broad buoyant bow, slender, double-ender stern and entry, and deep dragging keel. For their time the pinks were fast and weatherly sailers. They were the forerunners of the great New England fishing schooners built between 1860 and 1920.

THE CONSTRUCTION OF A WOODEN SHIP *ca 1730*

This generalized view of a wooden ship
depicts major structural elements
common to ships built from 1600 through
about 1825. The particular configuration
shown is approximately that of a small,
(6th rate) English warship of the early
1700's. The vessel would have been
about 100' on deck and about 25' in beam.

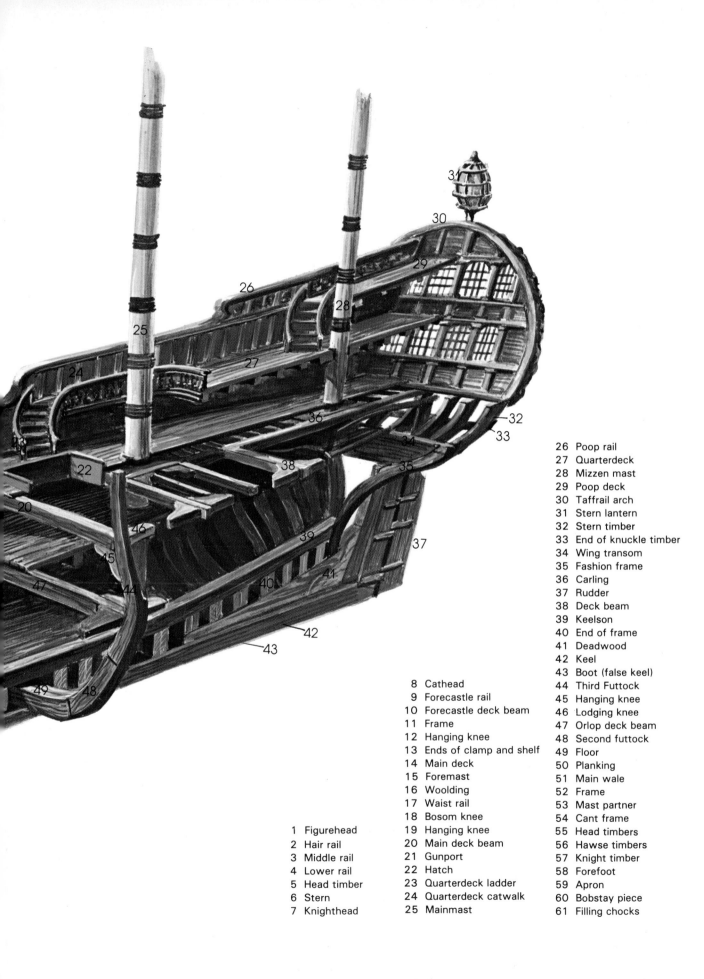

8	Cathead
9	Forecastle rail
10	Forecastle deck beam
11	Frame
12	Hanging knee
13	Ends of clamp and shelf
14	Main deck
15	Foremast
16	Woolding
17	Waist rail
18	Bosom knee
19	Hanging knee
20	Main deck beam
21	Gunport
22	Hatch
23	Quarterdeck ladder
24	Quarterdeck catwalk
25	Mainmast

1	Figurehead
2	Hair rail
3	Middle rail
4	Lower rail
5	Head timber
6	Stern
7	Knighthead

26	Poop rail
27	Quarterdeck
28	Mizzen mast
29	Poop deck
30	Taffrail arch
31	Stern lantern
32	Stern timber
33	End of knuckle timber
34	Wing transom
35	Fashion frame
36	Carling
37	Rudder
38	Deck beam
39	Keelson
40	End of frame
41	Deadwood
42	Keel
43	Boot (false keel)
44	Third Futtock
45	Hanging knee
46	Lodging knee
47	Orlop deck beam
48	Second futtock
49	Floor
50	Planking
51	Main wale
52	Frame
53	Mast partner
54	Cant frame
55	Head timbers
56	Hawse timbers
57	Knight timber
58	Forefoot
59	Apron
60	Bobstay piece
61	Filling chocks

THE BRIGANTINE LEON

Leon was a small merchantman built in 1880 at Larvik, Norway. She was 110.7 feet long, 28 feet in beam, and 13.2 feet deep. The Leon exhibits clipper-like lines and the characteristic features of later nineteenth century sailing ships. Deckhouses provided better lit spaces for the main cabin aft and for the galley "caboose" at the foremast. Deckhouses left maximum space below deck for cargo. The forward companionway hatch leads down to the forecastle. This 3/16'' = 1'0'' model of the Leon by Bob Pranka is a complete plank-on-frame rendering in a variety of exotic woods. No glue was used in the construction, all parts fastened with treenails and other mechanical bonds.

Model by D. Dressel

FAIR AMERICAN - 1776, 1/4 = 1'0".
Among several ships of the period christened *Fair American* was this 14-gun brig
thought to be the ship captured by the British during the American Revolution.
Sharp and wide of beam, the hull lines of the vessel anticipate the design ideas to
be incorporated later in the famed Baltimore clippers. The ship was 80'8'' in
overall length, 24 feet in beam and 9 feet in depth.

Major components of
THE IRON HULL
THE STAR OF INDIA

This cutaway shows the major components of an iron
hulled ship of the mid 1800's. The engineering premise of
such hulls was to think of them as truss girders covered
with plates. The plating strakes overlapped one another
resulting in a set of "inside plates" and "outside plates."

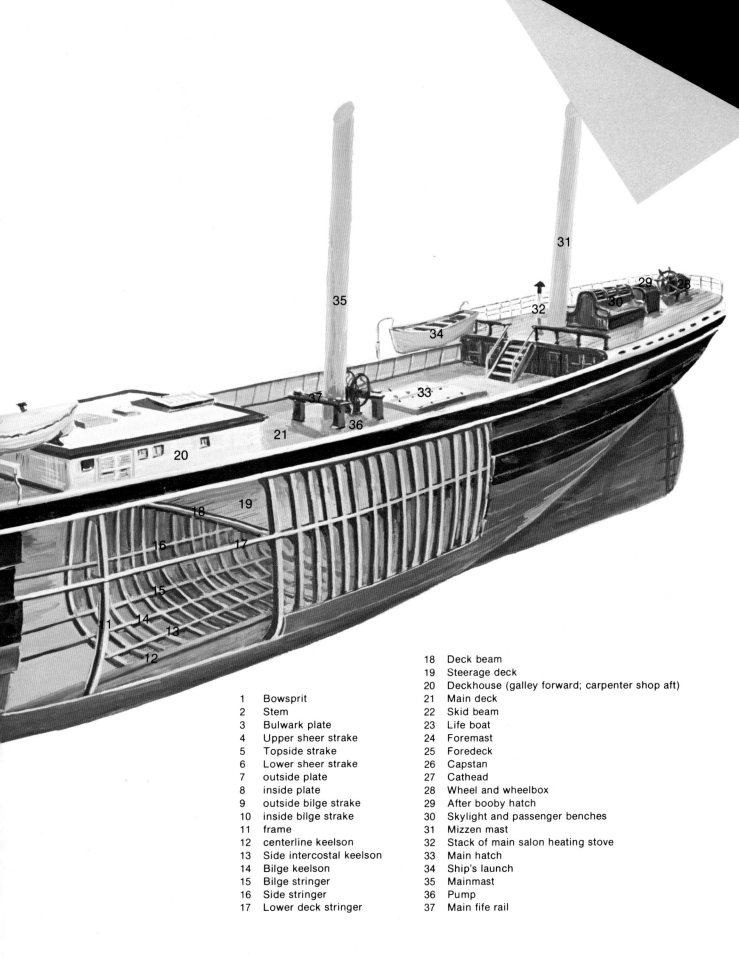

1	Bowsprit
2	Stem
3	Bulwark plate
4	Upper sheer strake
5	Topside strake
6	Lower sheer strake
7	outside plate
8	inside plate
9	outside bilge strake
10	inside bilge strake
11	frame
12	centerline keelson
13	Side intercostal keelson
14	Bilge keelson
15	Bilge stringer
16	Side stringer
17	Lower deck stringer
18	Deck beam
19	Steerage deck
20	Deckhouse (galley forward; carpenter shop aft)
21	Main deck
22	Skid beam
23	Life boat
24	Foremast
25	Foredeck
26	Capstan
27	Cathead
28	Wheel and wheelbox
29	After booby hatch
30	Skylight and passenger benches
31	Mizzen mast
32	Stack of main salon heating stove
33	Main hatch
34	Ship's launch
35	Mainmast
36	Pump
37	Main fife rail

MODERN YACHT - 1935, 1/4" = 1'0"
The Yachtsmen of the twentieth century adopted the
gaffless Bermuda or Marconi rig for its ease of handling.
High masts, low centers of gravity and deep keels
compensated for the loss of the gaff header's sail area. Allan
Weiss made this 1/4" = 1'0" model of the 50 foot Stevens
Yacht, Eagle launched in 1935.

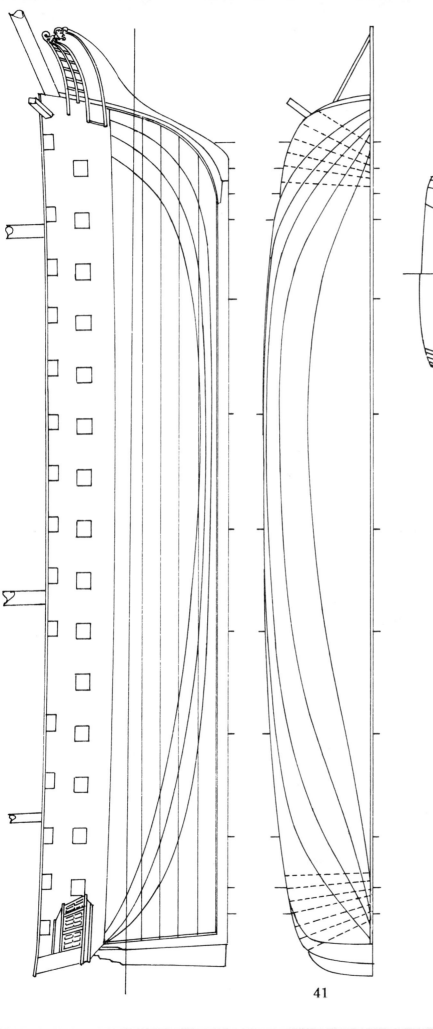

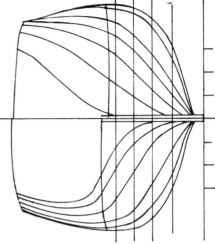

Lines of Continental Frigate **CONGRESS** - 1776 28 Guns, 682 Tons
Length between posts -126'-3½"
Length of keel (for tonnage) - 105'-4"
Breadth - 34'-4"
Depth in Hold - 10'-5½"

The fate of the *Congress* reflected the desperate plight of the American Colonials in the early stages of the Revolution. She was one of five 28 gun frigates authorized for construction under the Rhode Island Navy Bill of 1775. She was built and launched at Poughkeepsie, New York on the Hudson River but never finished. General Burgoyne, at the time she was launched, was advancing down Lake Champlain toward the Hudson with a large army threatening to connect with other British forces occupying New York. It seemed certain that the *Congress* would fall prize, so both to prevent this and possibly blockade the advancing British for awhile, she was scuttled about ten miles down river from where she was built.

41

DETAILS OF
WOODEN SHIP CONSTRUCTION

T he technique of building a wooden ship evolved from the early reed bundle vessels of the pre-Egyptians through a sequence of events which finally culminated by 1400 in a common Pan-European technology. The methods and terminology in use by 1400 are in essence the same as we use today. The method begins with the laying of a keel to which is fitted a stem and sternpost. Prefabricated frames are then setup along the length of the keel to form a skeleton structure. The skeleton is covered over with a skin of planks or plates. The method is recognized as *plank-on-frame* construction and, while not every ship in the world is built this way, it applies to a large majority. This chapter is devoted to an examination of the structural details of a wooden plank-on-frame vessel.

LOFTING

The construction of a ship begins with the translation of the architect's lines drawings to the full scale patterns for the actual structural components. The process is called *lofting.*

The lofting of the keel, stem, and sternpost is a matter simply of expanding to actual size the shapes given in the profile plan, while the patterns for the individual frames must be interpolated from the sections given in the body plan. The latter task is by far the larger and more demanding of the two.

Often the floor of a large room, designated the *loft*, was the scene for this large scale drafting. To one side a stripe was painted to serve as the keel reference line. The rest of the architect's grid of waterlines and buttocks would be laid out with taut strings. Then boards would be sprung under the grid in positions matching the frame being lofted. The shaped boards became the pattern for the final timber.

The plots for the frame came from an extension of the architect's lines plans. Verticals drawn in the profile and half breadths at each frame yield intersections with the buttock lines and the waterlines. Thus for each frame one has a plot of points up and out from the keel intermediate to those represented in the architect's body plan.

Plots for the rest of the important timbers followed similar procedures.

Modelers when constructing fully framed vessels use precisely the same methods except for the demands imposed by their miniature scales.

PLOTTING THE SHAPE OF FRAMES
FROM THE LINES DRAWINGS

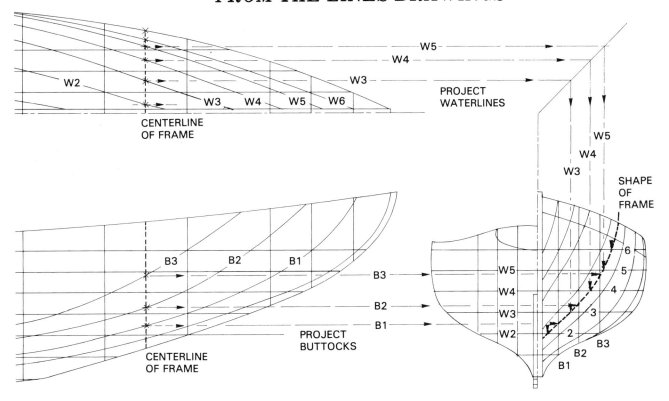

The plots for all of a ship's frames are derived from the lines drawing by drawing perpendiculars across buttocks and waterlines at the frame centerlines. Intersections of the frame centerlines with the buttocks and waterlines provide distances which are plotted on the body plan. The shape of each frame parallels the closest body section.

ROOM AND SPACE

Room and space is the naval architect's term for the center-to-center spacing of a ship's frames. The term derives from the Scandanavian *rum* which was used as a unit of measurement for a ship's length, and represented the distance between two rowing thwarts.

In the eighteenth century, rules for ship construction were laid out by the British Admiralty for warships, and by Lloyd's Register for merchant ships. Among these rules were those for room and space. A warship's room and space was to be .0172 times the length of the ship between the posts. The factor for a merchant ship was .027. The width of the frames in both cases was .47 of the total room and space. Thus from

about 1750 onward, naval ships, regardless of size, always had 58 frames, not counting cant frames, while merchant ships had 37. Though the decimal formulas for room and space did not become official until the eighteenth century, earlier ships probably conformed closely with this specification. The early shipwrights, as we have said, laid out a ship's hull with geometry, e.g., progressively dividing and subdividing lengths with the use of a compass and straight edge. The peculiar decimals of the later years were derived from earlier geometrical methods. These traditional formulas held sway in shipbuilding circles until the results of modern investigative science began to challenge their validity in the early nineteenth century.

SCANTLINGS

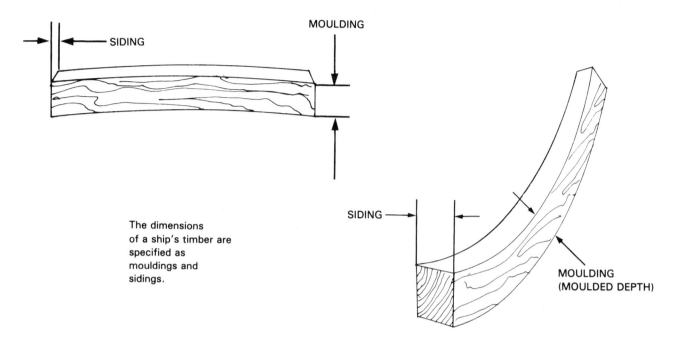

The dimensions of a ship's timber are specified as mouldings and sidings.

It is not enough for the shipbuilder, of course, to simply know the outside shape of a member. He must also know its thickness and general massiveness. Such specifications are known as *scantlings*. It was not uncommon to find ships made from the same lines with completely different performance characteristics because of different *scantlings*. One ship might have especially light scantlings, another very heavy. Merchant ships as a rule were made of lighter scantlings than warships of comparable size.

Naval architects, as well as prospective ship owners, spent considerable effort in specifying ship scantlings because unless they did, they were likely to fall prey to some unscrupulous economics by the shipwrights. Business then, as now, was business.

Today a significant portion of a ship's scantlings are spelled out in a special drawing called the *midship section*. In this single drawing it is possible to show the thickness of frames, planking, keel, and so on at the widest section of the ship, while calling out the variations of these

members at more forward or aft locations. The midship section is supplemented with other structural detail drawings as required.

This comprehensive practice, however, only became common in later years. Blueprints did not come into use until well into the nineteenth century prior to which there was no practical way to reproduce working drawings for use in the shop. In the early years, scantlings were spelled out in words, while hull designs were rendered in models. Beyond this, the old shipwrights designed their ships as they built them using materials as best they could to satisfy rather loose contract specifications.

Among the terms used in specifying a ship's scantlings are *mouldings*, and *sidings*. A moulding is the thickness of a timber in the vertical plane; a siding in the horizontal plane. Thus we read that a ship's keel has a moulded depth of 18 inches, sided 12 inches, and a sternpost is, "British oak - sided 10½ inches, moulded at keel - 19 inches, at top - 10¾ inches, 1 piece."

MATERIALS

Oak from the earliest times to the end of the wooden ship era was the preferred building material for most of a ship's structure. Keel, frames, planking, deck beams, carlings, and many other parts were almost always made of oak. When oak was not available, elm was considered an acceptable substitute. East Indiamen built in the Far East were made of teak.

The fabulous Mackay clipper ships of the 1850's are examples of craft partly built of less expensive, soft wood. The decision to compromise on materials for these ships was justified by the fact that a handsome profit could be made on them within the ten years they were expected to last. But for all their short lives, these ships were nonetheless superbly built and amazingly strong.

In the early days, shipwrights carved frames and other curved structural members from timber shaped naturally somewhat like the component. Later as timber resources diminished and ships grew in size, this practice became impractical giving way to built-up frames and other structures. Smaller elements such as knees, knuckles, breast hooks, and the like, however, continued to be built from naturally grown timber forms. In America, hackmatack, a variety of larch, provided a good source of natural "knee" shapes.

FASTENINGS

Timbers and planks were fastened together with iron bolts, nails, and wooden pegs called treenails or "trennels." Nails were really more like rivets. Holes were drilled through the timbers to receive them, after which the nails were driven home and cleated back on one side.

Treenails were used everywhere except in places where only the special strength of iron was required. Treenails driven into drilled holes of adjoining members expanded when wet to form solid watertight joints, while sharing the same ratios of expansion and contraction as the surrounding timber.

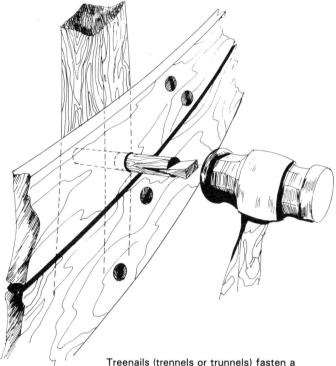

Treenails (trennels or trunnels) fasten a ship's timbers and planks together. Treenails were wooden dowels from one to three inches in diameter driven through holes drilled into the timbers often with expansion wedges slotted in either end.

Treenails fasten down the deck planking on the *Star of India*.

CAULKING

Hulls were made watertight by filling the cracks between the planks with hemp or other fibrous material soaked in tar and pitch. For many years, oakum payed over with hot pitch was the standard caulking material. Oakum was old, tarred rope picked apart into loose, bristly strands. A standard minor punishment for a miscreant crewman was to be sentenced to picking oakum, a boring job that painfully flayed the fingers. Richard Dana tells us in *Two Years* *Before the Mast* that on wet days when other work couldn't be done, the crew was set to picking oakum just to keep them busy.

To caulk a ship, soaked oakum was pounded into the seams with a light sledge hammer, and a chisel-shaped caulking iron. Since the planks swelled when wet, care was taken not to caulk the seams so tightly that structural damage would take place once the ship was afloat.

SHEATHING

The mighty wooden ships that weathered Cape Horn in winter and resisted assaults by cannon and fire, forever fought a losing battle against a living nemesis - teredo worm. Wooden ships to this day suffer the encroachments of these tropical seaborn termites which have been known to literally eat the bottom out of a ship.

In the early days of worldwide maritime activity, attempts were made to control the ship worms by adding extra layers of sacrificial fir planking to ship bottoms, or applying thick coats of tar mixed with horse hair and other materials. Anthony Deane tried lead sheathing but this approach set up galvanic currents which chewed away underwater iron fittings. Nothing worked really well until copper bottom plating was tried.

After 1780, copperplate sheathing became the accepted method of discouraging worm attack. Copperplate sheathing stayed in use into the twentieth century when it gradually was replaced by modern protective paint coatings.

Nothing so far, however, has managed to completely thwart the scourge of the teredo as owners of modern wooden craft testify.

COPPER SHEATHING - After 1780 the bottoms of ships were sheathed with copper plates as a defense against shipworms. Art Robinson's model of the Danish frigate *Jylland* of 1861 shows how the plates were overlapped bow to stern, and from the top down as shingles on a house. Copper nails were used since a different metal would have caused galvanic corrosion.

PAINTS AND FINISHES

Before 1850 there was no such thing as commercially prepared paint. Wherever paint was used it was mixed on the spot by the painter-craftsmen, and it was relatively far more expensive than it is today. So it is understandable that paint as such was used conservatively in shipbuilding.

Wooden hulls were sealed from the elements with pitch "tar." The term *tar*, so frequently mentioned in maritime history, should not be confused with the usual, modern idea of "tar." The tar used today for roofing or road building is in fact coal tar. The old seaman's tar was a variety of gum turpentine derived from certain kinds of tree sap. Pitch pine as well as other pine species were the most important sources of it. The sticky ooze from a wounded pine tree once melted down became varnish. It dried to a hard durable finish when applied paint-like to the wood of a ship.

The initial applications of "tar" left the wood a more or less natural color. With time the varnish oxidized darker and darker, and as more and more coats were added the color of the ship turned to a warm black.

The bottoms of ships were further coated with tallow, a yellow white wax-like material obtained from animal fat. Since tallow will not dissolve in water it makes an excellent waterproofing agent. Tallow was and is well known as a material for the making of candles. Dissolved in alcohol or turpentine, tallow was brushed onto the ship and left to dry to a hard surface.

Turpentine, or refined tar, and tallow were both used in paint, except that paint included at least two or three more ingredients. To make paint (then as now) a finely ground pigment was thoroughly mixed with a vegetable oil, most often linseed oil. The paste mixture was then thinned with varnish and turpentine, and small amounts of "drier" were added.

The pigments used were those found naturally in the earth. Reds were made from iron oxides; yellows from sulphur; blue and green from copper and chromium oxides, though, of course, the modern chemical names of these materials were unknown to the old painters.

The colors produced with the pigments were, by modern standards, rather dull. The brightest yellow obtainable was a mustard color or "yellow ochre." The brightest red, a brick red, and so on. The brilliant modern paint hues for the most part obtain from dyes, most of which have been developed in our own century.

So such paint as appeared on old ships was rather drab to begin with, while time darkened it in the same way it darkened unpigmented varnish.

In our own day, we are accustomed to ships painted to a clearly defined waterline. This practice only became common during the latter 1800's.

KEEL, STEM AND STERNPOST

A ship's keel is her backbone providing a major portion of the hull's longitudinal strength.

The keels of smaller vessels were (and are) made of a single, carefully hewn timber. Larger keels necessarily were pieced together, the joints scarphed for maximum strength.

The stem and sternpost are scarphed to the keel at either end and reinforced with knees. The outer edges of the stem and keel are protected by a cutwater piece (gripe), and a false keel or shoe.

Inboard of the stem lies the apron and stemson, which provide the surface to which the planking is nailed. The apron and stemson continue the line of the keel rabbet, the groove cut out to receive the planks on each side. Fore and aft the frames of the ship arise from the keel higher than they do amidships, so the keel is built-up of solid timber in these areas. The sections are called the fore and after deadwood.

The sternpost is comparable in structure to the stem except that it may not have a protective outer shoe. Inboard the inner post provides the shelf for the planking attachment.

Toward the end of the sailing ship era, auxiliary engines came into use, and with them propellers. To accommodate a midship, single screw, as well as a rudder, a second sternpost was contrived aft of the first and called the *prick post.*

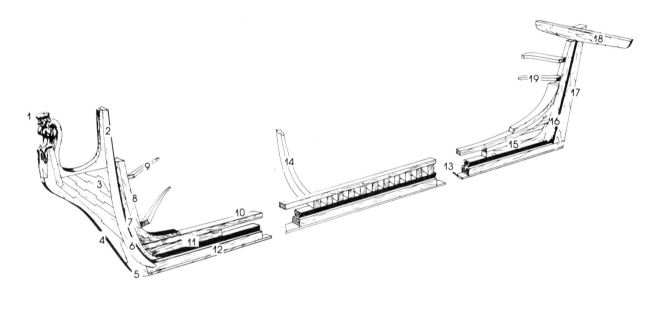

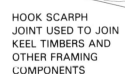

HOOK
SCARPH JOINT

HOOK SCARPH
JOINT USED TO JOIN
KEEL TIMBERS AND
OTHER FRAMING
COMPONENTS

1. Figure Head
2. Stern
3. Filling Chocks
4. Bobstay Piece
5. Gripe
6. Forefoot
7. Apron
8. Stemson
9. Breast Hooks
10. Keelson
11. Fore Deadwood
12. Keel
13. Boot (False Keel)
14. Frame
15. After Deadwood
16. Inner Post
17. Stern Post
18. Wing Transom
19. Lower Transoms

Henry Bridenbecker's plank-on-frame model of the brig *Irene* of 1806 exhibits the structure of frames through the use of vari-colored woods.

The *Jylland* was one of the earliest ships fitted with a *prick post* aft of the sternpost to accommodate a midship propeller.

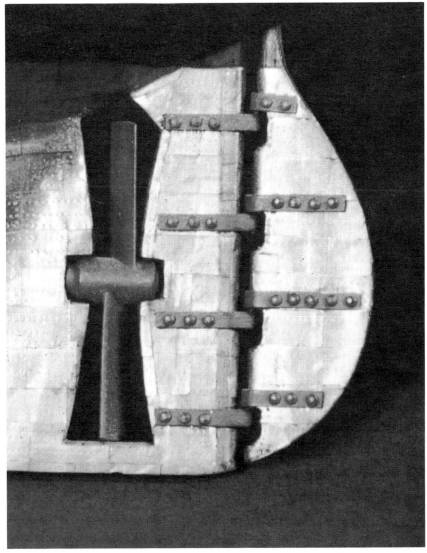

FRAMES

A ship's frames for most of history were composite structures consisting of the floors and a series of futtocks bolted and treenailed together. The frames straddled the keel and were treenailed to it. On top of them was laid another longitudinal member, the keelson, which followed the "line of floors" up to the stem and sternpost above the deadwood. The heavy stem and stern knees connect the keelson to the two posts.

At the bottom edge of each frame next to the keel, holes were bored so that bilge water would flow to the lowest level of the ship where the pump could remove it. The holes were called *limbers*. The inner ceiling planks just above the limbers, called limber boards, were made removable so that this lowest place in the bilge could be cleaned out from time to time. Sometimes chains were strung through the limbers so that a pull back and forth could keep the holes unclogged.

Frames tapered from keel to rail when viewed either in section or broadside. For most of the ship's length, the frames crossed the keel under the keelson as complete units from side to side, and were known as *full frames*. Toward the stern, as the rise of floors becomes more acute, the frames were built in two halves, and therefore called *half frames*.

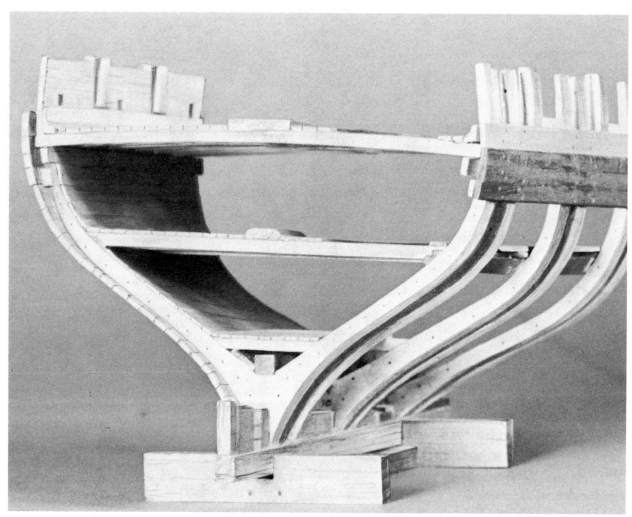

Sections of *Irene* show how half frames are joined to the stern deadwood, the clamp strakes supporting deck beams, and the variations in thickness of ceiling, bottom planking, and wales.

FRAMES

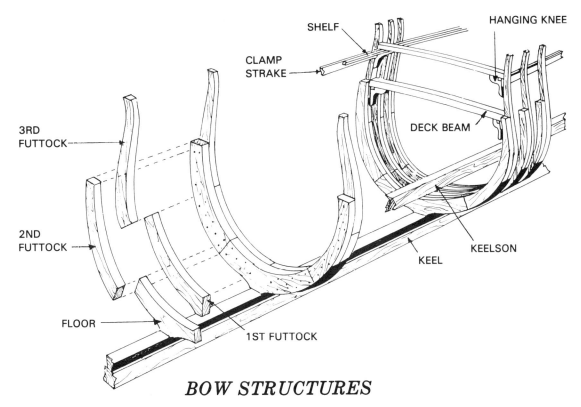

SHELF

CLAMP STRAKE

HANGING KNEE

3RD FUTTOCK

DECK BEAM

2ND FUTTOCK

KEELSON

KEEL

FLOOR

1ST FUTTOCK

BOW STRUCTURES

A solid mass of *head timbers* comprise the first few frames aft of the stem, followed by a number of *cant* frames, so called because they join the keel at other than right angles.

BOW STRUCTURES

The bow of a ship displays an especially strong structure since it was the bow that received the heavy brunt of the ship's forward motion. The bow structure had to support the pressure of the anchor cables, the mainstay, the bowsprit, and forestay.

For a distance aft of the stem, therefore, the frames were a solid mass of timber. The first frame was packed close beside the stemson. Next in line came the *knight timbers*, whose upper ends, called *knightheads*, protruded above deck level, served as attachments for various lines and cables, and provided lateral reinforcement for the bowsprit. Adjacent to the knight timbers were the *hawse timbers* through which the holes for the anchor cables were drilled. The array, if viewed from the top, could present a fan-like pattern of timber emanating from a point near the end of the keel, or in bluff-bowed ships, a row running parallel with the keel and ending at the first cant frame.

Cant frames were so called because they were mounted at an angle to the keel (canted) rather than straight across as in the case of the midship frame and most of the others. Cant frames occurred where the shipsides were radically out of parallel with the keel, and were so arranged that the faces of the frames could accept the run of the planking without excessive bevelling. The bows of older ships might have three or four sets of cant frames after the solid bow timbering. The sleeker bows of later ships might have one or two at most and sometimes none.

Finally, the bow was reinforced with breast hooks. The breast hooks were "v" shaped timbers often formed of natural crooks of trees, mounted across the stemson and the forward timbers like cleats or cross battens tying the rest of the bow structure together.

The *eking* timbers were in effect breast hooks that also served to support the bow end of the deck planking.

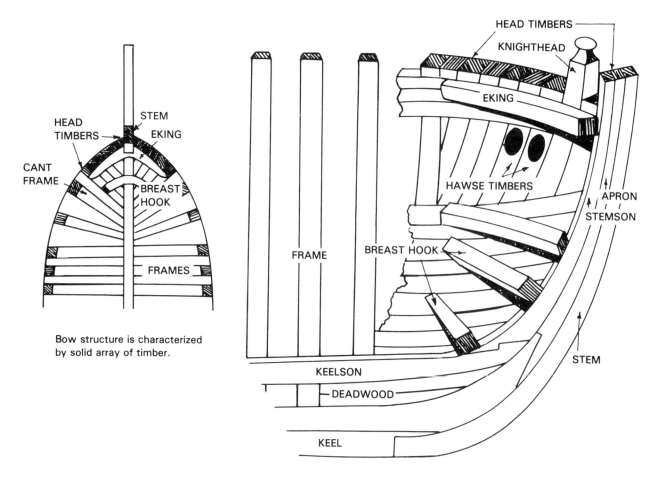

Bow structure is characterized by solid array of timber.

This Spanish galleon of around 1600 exhibits the broad, "square tuck" stern typical of ships built before 1630 when Phineas Pett introduced the "round tuck."

STERN STRUCTURES

The sterns of ships built after 1650 are the most complex structures in wooden ship construction.

Prior to 1650, the taffrail was a simple plane defined by the aftermost frame of the vessel. Longitudinal planks ended on the last frame, and stern planks connected either side of the frame straight across the slightly raked sternpost. This construction was referred to as the "square tuck" and applied to most European vessels. Then Phineas Pett introduced the "round tuck" stern in England about 1650.

The round tuck evolved from the wish to create a hull with a finer run and one which could take a following sea less brutally than the squared-off, flat, backside. Ships with square tuck sterns lived in continuous danger of being pooped, while at best they were cranky sailors.

The stern counter or overhang was developed to direct following water down under the hull.

The basic structure of the round tuck that Pett devised can be found with variations in almost all of the English ships built through 1860,

and constituted Pett's most notable contribution to naval architecture.

There are two key elements — the wing transom and the fashion frame. The wing transom mounts like the cross of a "T" across the inboard face of the sternpost. It is a solid timber shaped like a flattened out frame consistent with the lines of the rest of the ship. Its top edge provides the after shelf for the main deck; the under edge provides the terminus for the bottom planking.

The fashion frame is the aftermost true frame of the ship and is unique in that it is both a cant fame (angled aft from the keel in top view), and raked (slanted aft from bottom to top when viewed from the side). It arises from a point in the after deadwood somewhat forward of the inner post then curves up and aft connecting to the outer corners of the wing transom, then continues up to the poop deck rail.

The stern overhang or *counter* was built out from the wing transom by a system of stern frames running more or less parallel with the keel. These frames were connected athwartship by *knuckle timbers* and tied into the shipsides higher up by *quarter logs*.

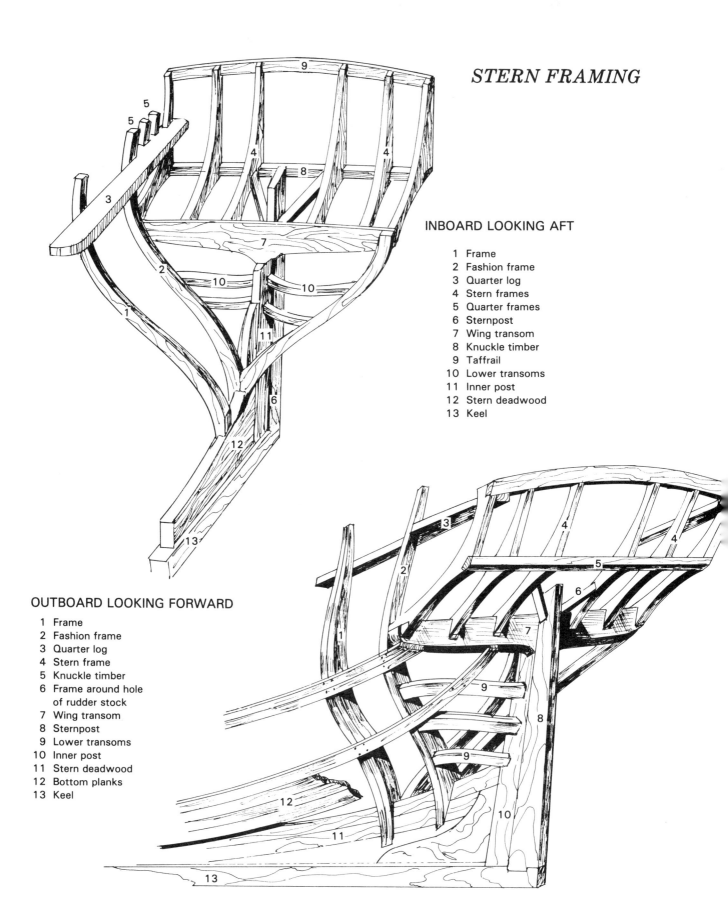

STERN FRAMING

INBOARD LOOKING AFT

1 Frame
2 Fashion frame
3 Quarter log
4 Stern frames
5 Quarter frames
6 Sternpost
7 Wing transom
8 Knuckle timber
9 Taffrail
10 Lower transoms
11 Inner post
12 Stern deadwood
13 Keel

OUTBOARD LOOKING FORWARD

1 Frame
2 Fashion frame
3 Quarter log
4 Stern frame
5 Knuckle timber
6 Frame around hole
  of rudder stock
7 Wing transom
8 Sternpost
9 Lower transoms
10 Inner post
11 Stern deadwood
12 Bottom planks
13 Keel

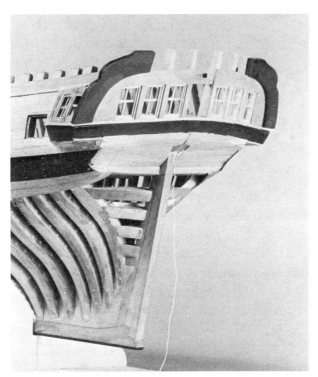

The stern of Bill Wick's *Oliver Cromwell* of 1776 shows the transoms of round tuck construction connecting the fashion frame to the sternpost. The wing transom shows at the bottom edge of the counter planking. Note the 'V'-shaped hole above the sternpost to accommodate the straight stock rudder.

Many smaller vessels from the earliest times were built as ''double-enders'' where the planking joined the sternpost the same way as at the bow. The small colonial American bark of 1620 illustrates the variation.

The stern of the American schooner *Hannah* of 1776 shows the flow of planking in typical "round tuck" stern construction.

Chapter Six
The
Iron
Hull

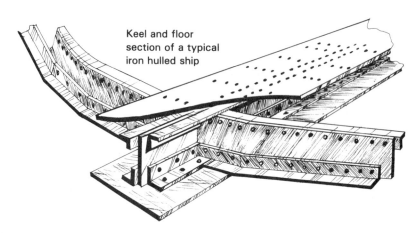

Keel and floor
section of a typical
iron hulled ship

W hoever heard of iron floating?" was the rallying cry of those in the early 1800's who could not accept a metallic threat to their beloved and ancient wooden ship tradition. At first the traditionalists had good reason, as well as prejudice, to resist iron as a shipbuilding material and only conceded the issue after nearly a century of debate and refinement of the new technology.

The first small experimental iron hulled vessel to astonish the world by not sinking appeared on the Thames in the 1790's, but a generation passed before the *Aaron Manby*, in 1820, become the first true iron ship in commercial service. She was a small steamer of about 116 tons which made regular runs between London and Paris up until 1855 when rust finally forced her into retirement. After the *Manby* was launched, a few more vessels were tried out, but the first large iron ship did not appear until 1843, when Isambard Kingdom Brunel's ship *Great Britain* came off the ways. The *Great Britain* was a screw propelled steamer, 322 feet long, displacing 3,270 tons.

It was Brunel's engineering of the *Great Britain* that set the precedents for true iron ship architecture. Previous efforts with iron were essentially cases of replacing wooden ship components with iron ones without consideration of the structural properties of the latter.

Brunel, before turning his attention to the design of ships, had been a railway engineer well acquainted with iron as a building material. He came to shipbuilding free of wooden ship preconceptions and so introduced innovations which lie at the heart of marine architecture to this day.

Before Brunel entered the picture, however, iron for all its apparent advantages, displayed discouraging disadvantages. First of all, it was difficult to shape by the then available casting and hot forging techniques. The structural members produced by these methods often cracked and became undependably weak. Second, it rusted at a formidable rate in salt water environments. Third, barnacles and other underwater growth, for some reason, grew more rapidly on iron bottoms than wood. Fourth, iron disrupted the operation of the magnetic compass. And, fifth, iron was comparatively expensive. Until Brunel's time, little could be gained by replacing wood with metal.

Several developments in the iron industry between 1784 and 1840 paved the way for Brunel. In 1784 Henry Cort devised a technique for changing brittle pig iron into a more flexible sort of wrought iron which in turn led to the first rolling mills.

The Stern of the iron hulled *Star of India*.

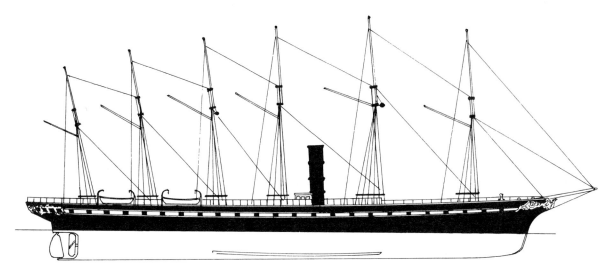

Isambard Kingdom Brunel designed the **Great Britain**, launched 1843. The first large ship to be built of iron using modern structural engineering principles.

Thereafter it was possible to produce structural iron in the forms familiar to us today as angle iron, 'T' bar, and 'I' beam. His "puddled" iron, as it was known, was precisely the material familiar to Brunel, the railway engineer.

Then in 1828, James B. Neilson, true to his Scottish heritage, found a way to reduce the price of puddled iron by inventing the blast furnace.

The combination of these events gave rise to extended experiments with iron truss girders.

The frames of the *Great Britain* were made of angle iron while "T" Bar and "I" beams connected them in the fore and aft direction into a large truss structurally consistent with a bridge girder. Since iron took up far less space than wood of comparable strength, Brunel divided up the hull into six watertight compartments with transverse and longitudinal bulkheads. These added both strength and a safety factor to his ship.

Brunel's work introduced several new terms to the shipbuilder's vocabulary. His new fore and aft framing members became known as *bilge keelsons, side intercostal keelson,* and *bilge stringers.*

After Brunel, iron shipbuilding gained momentum. Certain die-hards continued to believe that the only proper material for a ship was wood, yet conceded to the structural advantages of iron framing. Their thinking inspired the composite hull. The only essential difference be-tween the iron ship and the composite was that the latter was planked with wood. The famous *Cutty Sark* of 1860 had a composite hull.

The navy was the last to concede to iron because iron, as well as the steel of the nineteenth century could not withstand shell fire. The wooden ship, although armour plated, remained the staple of the sailing navy until the latter disappeared between 1880 and 1890.

The *Star of India* now moored as the main attraction of the Maritime Museum of San Diego is the last iron hulled sailing merchantman still afloat. She was launched November 14, 1863 at the yard of Gibson, McDonald and Arnold, at Ramsey, Isle of Man. Originally christened *Euterpe,* she began her career as a full-rigged ship and after a romantic world roving career of nearly 40 years, she was finally sold to the Alaska Packers Association of San Francsico. The Packers rechristened her *Star of India,* reduced her rig to that of a bark, and committed her in 1902 to annual up and down runs between San Francisco and Alaska. She lasted in this service until 1923 when, at last, twentieth century economics caught up with her. She is seaworthy to this day.

The *Star of India* is 205 feet long, 30 feet in beam, 23 feet 6 inches deep in the hold, and has deadweight tonnage of 1197.01. She is a living testament to the ingenuity of Isambard Brunel as well as to the skill of the Manx shipwrights who built her.

MODEL PLANS

Since ship models require thousands of hours of work, those who undertake to build them want the finished product to be worth the effort. Hence, they go to great lengths to be sure their plans are as accurate as possible.

Howard Chapelle, the distinguished maritime historian at the Smithsonian Institution, once chastised that group of ship modelers who insist on building "reconstructions" of vessels about which little more is known than their overall dimensions. Says he,

"In view of the huge quantity of plan material available it does not seem to me that there is little excuse other than obstinancy for 'reconstructed' models.

"... If you are going to spend a lot of time and effort on a model, at least be certain your plans are authentic and that the portions reconstructed are known to you and are understood. One ought to remember that accuracy in a model is of far more importance in giving a model value than fine workmanship alone."

Mr. Chapelle's position unquestionably applies to latter day ships and, in principle, to any ship model project regardless of era. Yet the farther back in history one goes, the less complete authentic plans for a given ship are likely to be.

For example, the *Mayflower* is a ship known to every American school child yet the records contain little more than her raw dimensions to tell us what she looked like. Several years ago the marine architect and historian, W.A. Baker, worked out a reasonable guess about the *Mayflower* based on what is known of seventeenth century shipbuilding practice in general. The result was *Mayflower II* currently on exhibit in Plymouth, Massachusetts.

Similar educated guesses lay behind the reconstruction of Sir Francis Drake's *Golden Hind* in San Francisco, and Raymond Aker, a preeminent authority on Drake and his ship, has taken strong issue with some of the guesses made in this reconstruction. In any case, no one pretends that these otherwise very scholarly efforts are actual "replicas" of the ships in question.

After 1736, more or less, the British Admiralty began to file drafts of the major ships in His Majesty's fleet so reasonably complete plans exist for these vessels. But here certain details of rig and furniture are obscure because they were not considered important enough to document.

The same situation occurs with even the most fully documented vessels of later periods. Mr. Chapelle's comprehensive study of American fishing schooners illustrates the point. He says, *"Documents and publications relating to the building of fishing schooners were found to be very scarce, and usually unreliable when found. Old marine catalogs were of some assistance, but a very great part of the fishing schooner hardware was made to 'fit the work' by the local shipsmiths. It was rare, then, to find a fitting that could be described by a catalog listing..."*

A *"... fairly complete specification of a 75-ton clipper schooner, probably a fishing schooner, built about 1875 ... had little on hardware and fittings ... Fragments of blueprints showing some fittings for the 1891 rigging of 'Grampus' were found, but these were suspect as not being typical of fishing schooners of this date..."*

We must add to the problem of incomplete documentation of historical vessels, the fact that most of them underwent continuous modification from the time of launching to the day they were retired. Thus even the most thorough set of plans can only represent a vessel at a certain point in her history. Today a number of maritime museums around the world feature restorations of actual historical ships. Without question these ships yield the most detailed plans presently available to modelers, and thousands of hobbyists as well as kit manufacturers have been drawn to them. Among these popular modeling projects are the *Cutty Sark*, and Nelson's *Victory* in England, The *Charles W. Morgan*, the whale ship in Mystic Connecticut; the *USS Constitution* in Boston, Massachusetts; and the *USS Constellation* in Baltimore, Maryland. Of these, the *Constitution* is probably the pet of American modelers, and particularly illustrates a vessel that underwent substantial modification during her lifetime.

The *Constitution* was launched in 1797 as one of the first six frigates of the brand new U.S. Navy. She subsequently suffered combat damage, was rerigged several times, carried various numbers of guns, was twice decommissioned and recommissioned, and finally in 1871 was hauled out and completely rebuilt. Little of her present restored condition reflects her appearance at the date of her launch. Model plans most always describe her as she looks today.

Thus, in spite of Mr. Chapelle's indictment of "reconstructions", all models are to some extent dependent on informed guesswork. The best models are those where the modeler has backed his decisions with intensive research and historical perception.

The plans included with ship model kits are often simplified though the good ones represent accurate scholarship as far as they go. No kit plans are intended to be used for plank-on-frame construction so they declare nothing about the ship's internal structure, though some lines drawings are sufficient to allow for the lofting of frame timbers if the modeler should wish to do so. Generally, however, kit plans are insufficient for a plank-on-frame project.

The wheel box, wheel and binnacle of the *Star of India*.

REFERENCES

Abell, Sir Westcott
The Shipwright's Trade
Cambridge, MA, 1948

Anderson, R.C.
Seventeenth Century Rigging
London, 1955

Baker, W.A.
The Development of Wooden Ship Construction
Quincy, MA, 1955

Bass, G.
*A History of Seafaring from
    Underwater Archaeology*
London, 1972

Botting, Douglas
The Pirates
Alexandria, VA, 1978

Bowen, John
Scale Model Sailing Ships
New York, 1978

Campbell, G.F.
Jackstay
Bogata, NJ, 1962

Chapelle, Howard I.
The American Fishing Schooners 1825-1935
New York, 1973

Charnock, J.
History of Marine Architecture
London, 1802

Cutler, Carl C.
Greyhounds of the Sea
Annapolis, 1930

Dana, Richard Henry
Two Years Before the Mast
London, 1912 from original of 1869

Davis, C.G.
The Built-Up Ship Model
New York, 1975 (reprint)
Ship Model Builder's Assistant
New York, 1970 (reprint)
Ships of the Past
New York, 1929

Durant, Will and Ariel
The Story of Civilization
Vols. 7, 8
New York, 1961, 1963

Edson, Merritt et al
Ship Modeler's Shop Notes
Washington, D.C., 1979

Grimwood, V.R.
American Ship Models and How to Build Them
New York, 1942

Haws, D.
Ships and Sea
Gothenburg, 1975

Heyerdahl, Thor
Early Man and The Ocean
New York, 1978
Kon-Tiki
Chicago, 1950

Howard, F.
Sailing Ships of War 1400-1860
Greenwich, 1979

Johnson, Gene
Ship Model Building
Cambridge, MD, 1961

Kemp, P.
The History of Ships
London, 1978
The Oxford Companion to Ships & the Sea
London, 1976

Kinney, Francis S.
Skene's Elements of Yacht Design
Eighth Edition
New York, 1981

La Fay, H.
The Vikings
Washington, D.C., 1972

Landstrom, B.
The Ship
Stockholm, 1961

Lever, Darcy
*The Young Sea Officer's Sheet Anchor
    or a Key to the Leading of Rigging*
London, 1819

Lubbock, Basil
The Western Ocean Packets
Glasgow, 1956

Mansir, A.R.
How to Build Ship Models, A Beginner's Guide
Dana Point, CA, 1979
A Modeler's Guide to Hull Construction
Dana Point, CA, 1980
A Modeler's Guide to Rigging
Dana Point, CA 1981

Melville, Herman
Moby Dick
New York, 1851

Millar, John F.
*American Ships of the Colonial
    & Revolutionary Periods*
New York, 1978

Morrison, Samuel Eliot
*The European Discovery of America
The Northern Voyages*
New York, 1971
*The European Discovery of America
The Southern Voyages*
New York, 1974
Admiral of the Ocean Sea
Boston, 1942

Nordbok, A.B. et al
The Lore of Ships
Gothenburg, 1975

Rogers, Woodes
A Cruising Voyage Around the World
New York, 1970 Republication of
    1928 & 1712 Editions

Ronnberg, E.A.R., Jr.
Benjamin W. Latham
Bogata, NJ, 1973

Underhill, Harold A.
*Plank-on-Frame Models and
    Scale Masting and Rigging*
Vols. 1 and 2
Glasgow, 1958

Webster, F.B.
Shipbuilding Cyklopedia
New York, 1920

Wiener, Philip O. and Noland Aaron
Roots of Scientific Thought
New York, 1957

Wilcox, L.A.
Mr. Pepy's Navy
New York, 1968

Periodicals:
    Model Shipwright
    Greenwich, England

    Nautical Research Journal
    Washington, D.C.

    Sea History
    New York

    Scale Ship Modeler
    Canoga Park, CA

    Ship Model Builder
    Memomenee Falls, WI

A

Aaron Manby, Iron steamship, 55
Aker, Raymond, 42
Alaska Packers Assn. of
    San Francisco, 57
Alberti, Leon Battista, 6
Anson, Commodore George, 23
apron, 49
area of lateral resistance, 14

B

Baker, Mathew, 6
Baker, William A., 42
ballast, 13
ballast keel, 13
Baltimore Clipper, 15,21,35
bark, *Star of India,* 57,36,37
Benson, William D., 3
bent frame construction, 26
Bernoulli, Daniel, 14
bilge keelson, 57
bilge stringer, 57
bobstay piece, 32,33,49
body plan, 5,7
boot (false keel), 32,33,49
bow structure, 32,33,52
breast hook, 32,33
breadth, main, 18ff
Bridenbecker, Henry, 25,28,29,30,51
Brunel, Isambard Kingdom, 55,57
Brunelleschi, Filippo, 6
Builder's Old Measurement
    (B.O.M.), 10
bulkhead, 28,57
buoyancy, 11ff
Burrell, William, 6
burthen, burden, tonnage, 8ff
buttocks, buttock lines, 5,7

C

caboose, 34
cant frames, 52
carling, carline of deck, 32,33
carvel planking, 27
cathead, 32,33
catwalk, 32,33
caulking 48
ceiling, 27
center of buoyancy, 11
center of effort, 13
center of gravity, 13
center of lateral resistance, 14
Centurion, H.M.S., lines of, 23,23

Chapelle, Howard, 42
chine, 17
Chinese War Junk, 28
chock, 32,33
clamp strake, 52
clamp stringer, 36,37
clinker built ships, 25
clipper ship, 15,24
components of ship motion, 16
composite hull, 57
Congress, continental frigate,
    lines of, 41
Constitution, U.S.S., 42,43
copper sheathing,
    bottom plates, 48
counter, 17
Cutty Sark, tea clipper, 57

D

dagger knee, 32,33
deadwood, 32,33,49
Deane, Sir Anthony, 6
    drafting procedure of, 8,18
deck beam, 32,33
displacement, 8ff
Doctrine of Naval Architecture,
    Deane, 8, 18ff
Dressel, Donald C., 35

E

Eagle, the yacht of 1935, 40
entry, of ships hull, 17
Euterpe, 57

F

Fair American the (1776), 35
false keel, 49
fastenings, hull, 47
fashion frame, timber, 53,54
filling chocks, 32,33
floor timber, 52; line of, 18
forecastle, 32,33
fore deck, 32,33
forefoot timber, 32,33
frame, 52
freeboard, 17
frigate, U.S., 41
Froude, William, 14,15
futtocks, frame timbers, 52

G

galleon, Spanish, 53
gravity, center of, 13
Great Britain, 55
Gresham College, 10
gripe: cutwater timber, 32,33

H

hackmatack, 47
half-breadth plan, 5,7
half frames, 51
hanging knee, 32,33,52
hawse timbers, 32,33
head timbers, 52
heave, component of ship
    motion, 16
Henry VIII, King of England, 6,8
Henry Grace a Dieu, 6
hog, hogging, hogbacked, 12
hydrodynamics, 14

I

inner post, stern timber, 49
Irene, brig of war, 50,51
iron hull, 55

J

James I of England, 6
Judson, Howard, 26
junk, Chinese, 28
Jylland, 48,50

K

Kalmar, Sweden,
    ship from, 25
keel, structure of, 49
keel plate, 55
keelson (kelson), 52
knight timber, 32,33
knighthead, 32,33
knuckle timber, 54

L

lateral resistance, area of, 14
Leon, the brigantine, 34
Lightning, clipper ship,
    lines of, 24
limber, 51
limber board, 51
Lloyd's Register, Lloyds of
    London, 9
lodging knee, 32,33
lofting, 44

M

main breadth, 18ff
main wale, 32,33
Malek Adhel, 29
*Maritime Museum Association
    of San Diego,* 57
mast partner, 32,33
Mayflower, 42
moulding, 46

N

*Naval Architecture,
    Deane's Doctrine of,* 8,18
nails, treenails, 47
Newton, Sir Isaac, 14

O

oak, 47
oakum, 48
overhang, 17

P

paint, 58
partner, of mast, 32,33
Pett, Phineas and family, 6,10
pinky schooner, 31
pinnace, 26
pitch, component of motion, 16
pitch, tar, 58
plank-on-frame construction, 27
Plimsoll markings, 9
Pranka, Robert L., 34
prick post, 50
Prince Royal, 6

Q

quarter frame, 55
quarter log, timber, 54,55

R

register tonnage, 10
rise of floors, 18
Robinson, Arthur, 48,50
roll, component of motion, 16
room and space, 45
Roos, Richard, 31
round tuck stern, 53
rum, 45
run of a ship's hull, 17

S

scantling, 46
scarf (scarph) joint of timbers, 49